ROAD ACCIDENTS

PREVENT OR PUNISH?

ROAD ACCIDENTS

PREVENT OR PUNISH?

J. J. Leeming, B.Sc.(Oxon), A.C.G.I., F.I.C.E., M.I.Struct.E., M.I.Mun.E., F.Inst. H.E.

With Contributory Chapters by

Dr G. M. Mackay, B.Sc., S., Ph.D., A.M. Inst.H.E.
Dr K. F. M. Pole, L.R.C.P. & S.,(Ed.), L.R.F.P. &
S.(Glas.) M.D.(Vienna)
Professor P. J. Fitzgerald, M.A., Barrister-at-Law

Commendation by

Lord Montagu of Beaulieu

Quinta Press

Meadow View, Weston Rhyn, Oswestry,
Shropshire, England, SY10 7RN

Visit our web-site: http://www.quintapress.com

ISBN 978–1–897856–29–1

First Published Cassell & Co. Ltd, now Cassell plc, a division of The Orion Publishing Group (London) 1969 S.B.N. 304 93213 2

Republished, reset, 2007

Set in 11 point Adobe Garamond Pro type

Printed and bound by Chris Fowler International Limited, London

This book is dedicated to the countless thousands who have died on the roads of the world as a result of the prejudices of a minority, as some reparation and in the faint hope that it may induce some government, somewhere, to begin trying to stop accidents

JOHN JOSEPH LEEMING, B.Sc., A.C.G.I., F.I.C.E., M.I. Struct. E., M.I. Mun. E., F. Inst. H.E., retired as County Surveyor of Dorset in 1964 after eighteen years of responsibility for the roads in that county. From 1924–46 he served the Oxfordshire County Council, as Resident Engineer on road works, Chief Engineering Assistant and finally Deputy County Surveyor. He is the author of *Road Curvature and Superelevation* and *Statistical Methods for Engineers* and has written numerous papers on bridge design, road curvature, and accidents. For these papers he has been awarded a Telford Premium by the Institution of Civil Engineers, the Institution Medal of the Institution of Structural Engineers and the Medal of the Institution of Municipal Engineers.

DR G. M. MACKAY, B.Sc., S.M., Ph.D., A.M. Inst. H.E., who writes on vehicles and accidents, established in 1963 at Birmingham University the Road Accident Research Unit within the Department of Transportation and Environmental Planning. He is in charge of a ten-man team consisting of traffic and mechanical engineers, doctors and a psychologist who conduct research into both accident causation and injury causation aspects of road accidents. The main research has concentrated on detailed on-the-spot investigation of collisions within a few minutes of their occurrence. In 1966 he was awarded a Ph.D. for research into urban road accidents and is now a senior research fellow of Birmingham University. His particular interests are vehicle design for crash protection for both occupants and pedestrians.

DR K. F. M. POLE, L.R.C.P. & S. (Edin)., L.R.F.P. & S. (Glas.), M.D. (Vienna), who writes on the driver from the medical aspect, has been a police surgeon to the Kent County Constabulary, which brought him into close contact with the medical aspects of traffic problems. He has lectured to the Institute of Traffic Administration and to ROSPA.

PROFESSOR P. J. FITZGERALD, M.A., who writes on the law and the motorist, was called to the Bar at Lincoln's Inn in 1951. He was elected Law Fellow of Trinity College, Oxford, in 1956, was appointed Professor of Law at Leeds in 1960, and in the University of Kent in 1966. He was editor of *Salmond on Jurisprudence* and has written an introductory work on Criminal Law.

Cover design: BRIAN ROLL

Commendation

I am delighted that *Road Accidents: Prevent or punish?* is being reprinted. I am very familiar with the work of John Leeming, who I much admired, and we are delighted to have his original papers in the library at Beaulieu. Leeming's book should be made compulsory reading for every politician, every police traffic officer, and every civil servant working in the transport sector. Perhaps then we would begin to make real progress towards Leeming's vision of roads that are safe and enjoyable for everyone and see the end of the fruitless war waged by the State against motorists.

LORD MONTAGU OF BEAULIEU
August 2007

Foreword to reprinted edition

When I started writing a series of articles based on *Road Accidents: Prevent or punish?* for the Association of British Drivers' newsletter, little did I realise the interest they would generate. John Leeming's scientific approach to analysing the causes of accidents, and his forensic demolition of the false beliefs underpinning much of road safety policy, clearly struck a chord with many. As a former traffic and road safety engineer myself, I am a great admirer of his work and was pleased to help bring it to the attention of a wider audience.

Publication of the articles on the ABD's website led to contact with John Leeming's son, David, who generously handed over his father's working papers to the Association. They were subsequently entrusted to the safekeeping of the National Motor Museum library at Beaulieu.

It is nearly forty years since *Road Accidents* was first published, but road safety policy in Britain (and much of the world) is no more enlightened now than it was then. If anything it is even more firmly grounded in ignorance and prejudice, with new technology providing more opportunities to punish drivers who break regulations that are often arbitrary or irrelevant. By republishing the book, I hope it will stimulate a new debate on the direction in which road safety policy is heading.

Many of the facts and figures and some of the methods described in the book are old, and the language may seem dated in places. But the principles that John Leeming followed in his research are just as valid now as they were then, including his refusal to reject perfectly good data that did not conform to a preconceived expectation. This contrasts with how research is often commissioned today, to provide 'evidence' to support a political decision that has already been taken. Also, driver behaviour is a function of human nature, which does not alter fundamentally with time.

I am most grateful to John Leeming's family, especially his son David, for their support in producing this reprinted edition, and to Jessica Purdue of the Orion Publishing Group, for her efforts to trace the copyright holders of Chapters 10 to 12. Finally, I would like to thank Dr Digby L. James of Quinta Press for making publication possible.

MALCOLM HEYMER
July 2007

Proceeds from the sale of this edition will be shared between the *Association of British Drivers* and the charity *Mobilise.*

The *Association of British Drivers* is a voluntary and non-profit-making organisation whose aim is to provide an active, responsible voice to lobby for Britain's beleaguered drivers. Details of the Association's aims, and how to join, can be found on its website at www.abd.org.uk.

Mobilise is a self-help organisation run for disabled people by disabled people, and concerns itself with the needs of disabled people, primarily by encouraging greater independence through enhanced mobility. It was formed in 2005 from the merger of the *Disabled Drivers' Motor Club* (of which John Leeming was an original committee member) and the *Disabled Drivers' Association.* More details can be found on the charity's website at www.mobilise.info.

CONTENTS

INTRODUCTION

The study of road accidents started in the early thirties, when the late Lt.-Col. G. T. Bennett, then County Surveyor of Oxfordshire, began to take an interest in them. He was the first to study them on the site, and to try to find out every fact associated with them. His work showed that the conventional attitude was one-sided, and was not based on a study of the facts. He was, of course, abused by the school of thought I have, in a later paper, called the 'lambaste the motorist school', and no attention was paid to him, except by a few members of the technology of which he was a founder-member, traffic engineering.

I was Bennett's chief technical assistant, and later his deputy, until I left Oxfordshire on appointment as County Surveyor of Dorset. I discussed his ideas with him many times, and when I went to Dorset I was able to test them on other roads. All the facts I was able to obtain, and all the information I could gather from my colleagues, tended to confirm their validity. This book is based on Bennett's work, and extends it.

So far as I know, it is the first book of its kind to be written by a professional engineer who has specialized in traffic matters. Strange and incredible as this may seem, I have spent forty years of my life *increasing the speed of traffic to reduce accidents, with some success.* The book will, therefore, run counter to many strongly held prejudices, and will come to many as a severe shock.

The present approach is to lay the whole blame on the driver, but I feel that one should not condemn a large section of one's fellow beings without there being very sound reason for thinking that they are in the wrong, and even then, only when that wrongdoing is clearly wilful and deliberate. If, as so often happens on the roads, it is due to failings inherent in human beings, still more if it is contributed to by others, it is surely our duty to help, and not to condemn. We must approach the problem in the spirit of the famous quotation I have put at the head of Chapter 1.

ACKNOWLEDGEMENTS

I AM most grateful to the many people who have helped me in the preparation of this book. I must specially thank my co-authors Drs Mackay and Pole and Professor Fitzgerald, and the County Surveyors of the following counties, who have supplied me with figures from which I have been able to prepare Table 10: Angus, Antrim, Berkshire, Brecknock, Buckinghamshire, Cambridgeshire, Cumberland, Devon, Dorset, Down, Durham, Essex, Gloucestershire, Hampshire, Herefordshire, Hertfordshire, Kent, Lancashire, Monmouthshire, Northamptonshire, Nottinghamshire, Oxfordshire, Pembrokeshire, Shropshire, Somerset, Staffordshire, East and West Suffolk, West Sussex, Warwickshire, Westmorland, Wiltshire, Worcestershire, the East, West and North Ridings of Yorkshire; also the City Engineer of London and the Borough Surveyors of Torquay and Workington. Some of them, particularly the County Surveyors of Lancashire, the West Riding of Yorkshire and Gloucestershire have done special studies for me, and I am most grateful to them. I must also include their staffs in my thanks, and especially Mr H. R. Battrick, who was my traffic assistant in Dorset.

I have also been helped with advice and information by the Director of Road Research and his staff, especially Dr F. Garwood; and also Professor R. J. Smeed; the editor of *Traffic Quarterly;* Professor Daniel P. Moynihan; the Commissioner, State Department of Motor Vehicles, Connecticut, U.S.A.; Mr Roy S. Hewitt; Dr T. C. Willett; and many others. Them I also thank.

Finally, I must pay a tribute to the memory of my old chief in Oxfordshire, the late Lt-Col. G. T. Bennett, on whose ideas I have based this book. If it has any good effect, this will be due to him.

I

SCHEME OF THE BOOK

'I may speak with every tongue that man and angels use; yet if I lack charity, I am no better than echoing bronze, or the clash of cymbals ... Charity is patient, is kind; Charity feels no envy ... takes no pleasure in wrongdoing, but rejoices at the victory of truth.'

St Paul, I Corinthians, Chapter 13. Trans. R. A. Knox

I. ARRANGEMENT OF THE BOOK

The subject is usually treated in the order of the Three 'E's of ENFORCEMENT, *Education,* and engineering, with almost all attention paid to enforcement, and engineering very much played down. I am going to arrange the book in the opposite order of Engineering, Education and Enforcement. This is because engineering is the only one of the Three 'E's in which we are able to find out the facts directly and in detail. The effect of the others is based merely on guesswork, or even on misrepresentation. Having some facts, we can then draw conclusions about the other two.

I shall start by explaining in simple terms how the statistician thinks, as so many of our conclusions depend on his methods. His case has rather gone by default, and the public has become so obsessed with Disraeli's notorious saying: 'There are lies, damned lies, and statistics' that people automatically distrust statistics, but this is based on a complete misunderstanding.

Some figures will be essential, but I shall only give those which are not ordinarily available, or are commonly suppressed. These will be needed to allay much misunderstanding. I shall then discuss Bennett's theory of accident causation, and, very briefly, the factor of chance.

There will then be four sections dealing with more specialized matters: the first by myself on the effects of road and traffic engineering, on signs, and on propaganda, then by Dr Mackay on the vehicle, Dr Pole on the driver from the medical aspect, and, finally, by Professor Fitzgerald on the law. All are specialists on their subjects.

Finally, I shall go on to discuss what we know and, far more important, what we do not know, and then propose a remedy.

2. TECHNICAL TERMS

I am afraid I cannot avoid using some technical terms from statistical methods and traffic engineering. These have more precise meanings than the usual words. To help the reader, I shall always define these terms when they are first met, when the terms will be printed in *italics*. The reference to the definition in the index will be printed in **bold type**. After definition, the word will only be used in the technical sense.

I can hardly avoid occasionally using a little very mild mathematics. I can only apologize to the hopelessly non-mathematical for this, and hope that they will take it on trust, and as an indication of the fact that the whole problem is not quite as simple as they may be inclined to think from some of the propaganda.

3. TRAFFIC ENGINEERING

Traffic engineering is defined as: '*That part of road engineering which deals with traffic usage and control, and includes traffic planning and the design of road layout.*' This extract from BS.892/1967 Glossary of Highway Terms is reproduced by permission of the British Standards Institution, 2 Park Street, London W.1.

This book is decidedly not a manual of traffic engineering, but I hope to convey to the non-technical reader some idea of the way in which a traffic engineer works in his approach to the accident problem, and how the relations of the law and the propaganda appear to him. It might perhaps be more precise if I said that I shall show how one traffic engineer has worked. The subject is not yet standardized, and there is much variation in approach. Possibly, also, not all of my colleagues would agree with me.

The impression may be conveyed—quite correctly—that it is a hit-and-miss affair. We are really working rather like a Sherlock Holmes or Lord Peter Wimsey, though, of course, without the omniscience with which a novelist can endow his characters. Each traffic engineer studying the problem is a research worker, evolving his methods for himself, and still contributing something to knowledge.

4. THE NEED FOR FACTS

Our basic approach must be to ask for FACTS AND ONLY FACTS. It is often said 'such-and-such *must* cause accidents', almost always with the addition 'so make it illegal!' But to this we must answer '*Does* it cause accidents?' 'Where are your facts?' 'On what evidence do you base your statement?' Usually, they have no facts and no evidence. The following is typical:

(1)   *Memo to Barbara*
'The Bishop of London spoke wisely yesterday about the sort of bad driving which causes accidents. Perhaps, Mrs Castle, you ought to conscript him on your panel of Road Safety experts. Nobody who has driven on American expressways could fail to agree with him in welcoming our own general speed limit. The Americans are decades ahead of us in knowledge of traffic problems (though not so much ahead of us in solutions) and if they find limits essential it is crazy, if not criminal, for our motor-car lobby to oppose them.

'The Bishop, Dr Stopford, says that he drives seven days in the week all over Greater London, and knows most of the main and secondary routes. He sees 'near-accidents' all the time, and guesses that most of these are caused by impatience, bad temper, pushy driving and skipping through the lights. He is dead (or perhaps more accurately alive) right. Mrs Castle. Please talk to him.' *London Letter in the* Guardian, *13.1.66.*

So! The Lord Bishop guesses, the Minister should be guided by his guess, and presumably people should be prosecuted on it. The Americans have speed limits and so should we.* But, as Hamlet said, 'Marry, this is miching mallecho; it means mischief'. It is of no practical use—and indeed, is often very harmful—to say that such-and-such *must* or *could* or *should* or *might* cause accidents. WE MUST KNOW IF IT DOES CAUSE THEM.

But we must go further. Even supposing that we have found that any proposed measure will stop accidents, we must next go on to ask how many it will stop, and then, *how many it will cause in its turn.* It is always possible—it does even happen—that a proposed remedy may be worse than the disease. I shall show that there is much reason to think that our present 'remedies' are themselves a large part of the reason why we have so many accidents.

Next, we must ask how much the remedy will cost, and then whether the money could be spent to better advantage in other ways of accident prevention.

---

* The author of London Letter has conveniently forgotten that many of the American speed limits are 'advisory'. See Chapter 7 below.

Finally, we must ask if the proposed remedy would be socially harmful.

5. THE STATE OF OUR KNOWLEDGE

We really know very little about the subject. I will try to indicate what we do know, and what is merely guesswork. Much of the book will consist in asking questions, and in throwing doubts on many things which are always taken for granted as proven facts. But until we can dispel the cloud of conjecture, unfounded statements, prejudice and—*horresco referens*—sheer downright lying, which has so confused the issue, we can never make any progress in reducing the accidents.

One great cause of our ignorance is the belief that because some statement has been made by a Lord, a Bishop (Qu. 1, p. 3), a Judge or an M.P. it must be true merely because that eminent gentleman has said it. *But it doesn't matter what these gentlemen have said. What matters is whether they are qualified by knowledge, and have the evidence to be able to say it.*

With all this clamour, the voice of the traffic engineer, who has studied the subject, and does know a little about it, passes unheard.

6. THE THREE 'E's

We are often told that the Three 'E's are the heart of the accident problem, but there is much truth in the comments of a witty American writer:

(2.) 'Had this article been written twenty years ago, it would have been stated positively that the Three 'E's—engineering, education and enforcement—constitute the answer to the traffic safety problem. Since that time, observation of their fighting many losing battles with the Three 'P's—pressure, prejudice and politics—has considerably shaken my faith in the Three 'E's as a cure-all. Like the boy in Mark Twain's story, who ran away from home because his father was ignorant, obstinate and opinionated, and returned three years later to be amazed at how much the old man learned in three years, I am amazed at the number of things I knew twenty years ago that aren't true now, and probably never were. While still of the opinion that the Three 'E's are an essential part of the correct approach, I have learned that they are not enough. We also need research, planning, administration, legislation, adjudication and financing, to name only a few.' *Hallie L. Myers, 'Promoting Traffic Safety in Indiana'. T.Q. October 1955 (see p. 7 for reference). (Mr Myers was Executive Director of the Indiana Traffic Safety Foundation.)*

This was written twelve years ago and, like Myers, I also have been learning in the interval, and go on learning. I would only differ from him in two ways. I think we have far too much legislation, and I would add the Three 'L's—Lies, Lethargy and Laws—to his Three 'P's. All six of these are killers.

The most important of his suggestions is research. There is too little of this. I am far from belittling the work which has been done in many countries, still less the excellent work done by my friends at the Road Research Laboratory. I feel, however, that if their devotion to research could overcome their discretion as civil servants, they would be the first to complain of the hampering effect of Myers's Three 'P's. Far too much of their time and limited resources has been taken up in studying the effects—if any!—of some sudden hunch on the part of a minister or politician. It is sometimes hard to resist the conclusion that these are not always dictated by zeal for Road Safety, but by political or personal motives, and they have taken the laboratory staff off really important work.

It is not good enough to say that the Three 'E's are all that we need, and leave it at that. We must ask: 'What kind of engineering do we need, what kind of education, and enforcement of what?' We must not take it for granted that any old thing will do, so long as we announce that we want to stop accidents, and that it involves more penalties for motorists. In particular we must ask—because these are the matters about which we know least—is our education good, and are our laws really calculated to reduce accidents? We have assumed that they are, but the tragedy of the situation is that they almost certainly are not.

7. BLAME

In the first part of the book, I shall exclude all consideration of blame, and will discuss it in a special chapter as a subject in itself (14, p. 196). Blame for accidents seems to me, as a traffic engineer, to be at best irrelevant, and at worst actively harmful. My object is to STOP ACCIDENTS, and I am not interested in blaming anyone.

Bennett and I have been accused of 'blaming the roads' for all

5

accidents, but neither of us has ever done this. What we have said is that *if such-and-such a road improvement had been done, certain accidents would not have happened.* That is all. It is just a statement of fact. Blame is irrelevant to that statement.

The obsession of attributing blame, especially blame to the motorist, is a dangerous red herring, and may thereby be the reason why the world is having so many accidents. It is, of course, very human to want to ·blame someone else, and to find a scapegoat. It saves a lot of thought, and deadens a sense of responsibility in those who have an uneasy feeling that they are not entirely free from guilt themselves.

It is very likely that in much of what follows, the mere statement of the facts will lead to the thoughts of blame. I hope these will be resisted. I shall not intend to do it until I reach Chapter 14. I repeat that, if I say that some measure or other will reduce accidents, I shall merely be stating facts, or drawing legitimate inferences. I hope the reader will follow me in dismissing the idea of blame until we reach the subject.

8. LITERATURE

There is an enormous literature on road accidents, but most of it is best buried in a merciful oblivion. People who write books about them do not think it necessary to know anything about their subject, or about scientific discipline, or statistical methods. I mention statistical methods because they are the essential tool for dealing with the matter. To discuss accidents without an understanding of them is like trying to do gardening without knowing how to use a spade or secateurs.

Of the serious literature, two books stand out above all others, and I shall make much use of them. These are the two Road Research Laboratory publications, *Research on Road Safety* and *Research on Road Traffic.* For brevity, I shall refer to these in the text as RS and RT respectively.

For the vast literature on Research into accidents, I refer the reader to the *Selected Bibliography on Road Accident Research* produced by the Department of Transportation and Environmental Planning of the University of Birmingham. This, together with its supplement, *A Review of Road Accident Research* from the same source, is available to serious students.

6

I shall keep references to the minimum, but I shall occasionally quote from the following journals, referring to them by the letters given here, after the name of the journal:

Traffic Engineering and Control (TEC), London.

Traffic Quarterly (TQ), The Eno Foundation, Saugatuck, Conn., U.S.A.

The *Listener* (L), The BBC, London.

The *Autocar* (AU), London.

The Times (T), London. *Times Law Report* (TLR)

The *Daily Telegraph* (DT), London.

The *Guardian* (G), London and Manchester.

When I make cross-references to other parts of the book they will be given in the text like this (3.2, p. 16), which refers to Chapter 3, Section 2, on page 16, the section on definitions. If a page is given in a reference the number will be that of the page in the reference, thus (RT, p. 418) refers to page 418 of *Research on Road Traffic*.

A reference in the text such as (Qu. I, p. 3) refers to Quotation No. 1 on page 3.

To avoid the tedium and waste of space in repeating lengthy titles some abbreviations will be made. *Ministry* will mean the Ministry of Transport in London. *Minister* will mean the Minister of Transport, unless reference is made to a specific minister, who will then be named. The RRL will mean the Road Research Laboratory, and HMSO Her Majesty's Stationery Office, the British Government's printing and publishing department. ROSPA is the Royal Society for the Prevention of Accidents.

I have used the first person singular when describing discussions with people and public bodies. That does not necessarily mean that the experiences happened to me personally, or that the places described were in Dorset or Oxfordshire—the two counties in which I have served—but all are authentic except for the omission of any clues to the identity of the people mentioned. If they did not happen to me, I can still vouch for the truth of the story. It will have come first-hand from some other road engineer, foolish though some of the stories may appear. There is an old and very true Lancashire saying: 'There's nowt so queer as fowk!' and some of those who lay down the law about road safety are queerer still!

2

STATISTICAL METHODS

'A man of science isn't trying to prove anything. He's trying to find out what will prove itself.'

G. K. Chesterton, 'The Blast of the Book', from
The Scandal of Father Brown

I. PRELIMINARY

This chapter may be difficult for some readers, but it is hard to see how this can be avoided. Statistical methods are essential to get any useful information, or to make use of what we have. We must also be able to get some inkling of when we are being deceived. I hope that those who are not mathematical will try to follow it as far as they can for it is very important.

The word 'proof'—so often misused—must be mentioned first, to clear away the lumber. In spite of the popular idea of him, the statistician does not use this word. He is like the scientist in the quotation above, though possibly even more sceptical. As evidence piles up, he may find that some conclusion or other can be accepted with ever-increasing confidence, till finally no reasonable person could reject it without forfeiting his claim to be called reasonable. But it is never impossible that something or other may turn up to upset the conclusion, though this may become more and more improbable. We may also find that some result looks reasonable and can be accepted on small evidence, but may be found to be less and less sound as evidence piles up, till finally the reasonable man can no longer accept it.

2. VARIATIONS

The whole subject depends on the fundamental fact that whenever we make a series of measurements of the same thing they will never all agree exactly. There will be variations—or *scatter*— among the individual measurements. Even if they are as precise as those astronomers make they will never agree exactly. Although the scatter may be very small, it will still exist. The precision will only affect the size of the variations. *There is no such thing as an exact or unique measurement.*

In traffic matters our scatter will be wide, because we are dealing with events controlled by a number of different factors, many of which we do not know, and also because one of them is that most unpredictable thing, human nature.

This means that we must not be surprised if our accident figures fluctuate from year to year. We often hear people saying: 'The deaths in our area have fallen by two or three compared with last year, argal* our propaganda has been good,' but unless the changes are large, or there has been some clear trend, we must disregard them. We expect them to happen, and would be surprised if they did not. If the accident figures always came out the same, year after year, the statistician would smell a rat, and might even suspect that something had gone wrong in the police department, a treasonable thought. Variations and fluctuations are inevitable, and we suspect their *absence* and not their presence. Their absence may mean bias—or worse.

Statistical methods are the science of studying and dealing with these variations.

3. AVERAGES

Everybody knows that in algebra we deal with a variable function for which the usual symbol is x, which we can give any value we wish. But in statistical methods we deal with a corresponding function which cannot be given any value we please. Ours will have a probability attached to it, and it will have a limited range which will cluster about a central value. We therefore call it the *variate* to emphasize the distinction.

This central value is called the *average,* though the statistician uses this word in a more generalized sense than the ordinary man. By it he means a roughly central value, and he uses several averages.

The conventional 'average' is a value obtained by adding up all the values of the variate and dividing by their number. Thus if we wanted the average speed we would add up all the speeds measured and divide this sum by the number of cars timed. The statistician calls this average the *mean.*

There are two other averages which are useful in traffic studies. The *median* is the central value, that is, the one which has half the total values of the variate larger, and half smaller, than itself, and

---

* This word 'argal' is a corruption of the Latin word 'ergo' meaning 'therefore', and is used for that word by some of Shakespeare's clowns. It is a useful word, and I shall use it for indicating conclusions reached on unsound evidence. *Therefore* we shall come across it a lot.

the *mode* is the value, or group of values, of the variate which occurs more frequently. I add 'group' because when we have large numbers it becomes almost impossible to deal with them individually, so we take them in *groups* of a convenient range of values of the variate. When dealing with timings of speed, I used groups covering four miles an hour, counting, for example, all cars doing between 24 and 28 miles/h together as if they were doing 26 miles/h. This saves much arithmetic, and in reasonable-sized samples does not involve any serious error.

The median and the mode are not easy to deal with mathematically, while the mean is, so the latter is the more commonly used average. But the other two are sometimes important. If there is any chance of confusion, it is better to specify what average is being used, and say the mean speed—or whatever is being measured—or the median speed or the modal speed, rather than just the average speed.

4. THE POPULATION AND ITS SCATTER

The statistician uses the word *population* to mean an infinite number of the observation he is studying. He does not confine the use of the word to people. His use of the word *infinite* also does not carry quite the full mathematical meaning of the word, but may mean a number which is large but is still possible to count.

He will locate his population by using the mean. Thus, using speed again, he will consider the speeds of an infinite—or very large— number of cars passing his observation point as his population. Then the mean speed of those he has timed will enable him to estimate what type of traffic he is studying, and to locate it on a diagram.

He will then want to know how this population is scattered about the mean. The existence of a mean necessarily implies that the population is scattered, and it also means that *roughly* half the population will be below, and half above the mean.

The measure of the scatter most frequently used is a function called the *standard deviation*. I will not enter into its mathematics here; it will be found in the Appendix (p. 223). Examples of its applications will be found at the end of this section and when we discuss the new blood-alcohol test. We can calculate the probability of occurrence of any value of a variate once we know the mean and the standard deviation.

If the scatter of the observations follows some reasonably orderly pattern, it is called a *distribution*. There are many of these, but the one most usually used is called the *normal,* and most of the tests used are based on it. It is symmetrical about the mean, and its mean, median and mode are all the same.

In the normal distribution we find that two-thirds of the observations will come within a range of one standard deviation on either side of the mean and 95% of them will fall within the range of two standard deviations on either side of the mean.

In a number of speed timings in Dorset, it was found that the mean speed was almost exactly 32 miles/h, and the standard deviation was almost exactly 7 miles/h. We would therefore expect that two-thirds of the cars passing would be less than 7 miles/h on either side of the mean, and so be travelling within the range of 25–39 miles/h, and 95% of the cars to be within 14 miles/h of the mean, that is, within the range of 18–46 miles/h.

5. THE SAMPLE

The population is usually an abstraction, perhaps represented by an elaborate formula, and is so large that we hardly ever deal with it in practice. The information we get will consist of one or more sets each of a small number of observations. These are called the *sample,* a familiar enough word for once used in a familiar sense.

A *random sample* is one so chosen that every observation in the population has had an equal chance of being included in it. A sample that is truly random will give us some useful information about the population from which it is drawn.

This is not as simple as it sounds, and it is not always easy to set up a random sample. One which is not random but has *bias*—again a familiar word used in a familiar sense—can be misleading. For this reason, a true statistician makes every possible effort to get his samples as random as possible, and if there is any doubt he makes it clear where the possibility of bias lies. On the other hand, many propagandists try to get samples as biased as possible, if the bias suits their ideas. They then sweep all the others unobtrusively under the carpet and breathe no word about the possibility of bias.

Just as we do not expect every observation to agree exactly with the others, we do not expect two random samples from the same population to agree exactly either. If they do, we again suspect bias.

Our commonest problem is that we have two or more samples of the same variate, and we want to know whether they are likely to be drawn from the same population. Alternatively, there may be some known difference in the conditions under which the samples have been drawn, and we want to know whether it has affected things. For instance, we may have timed traffic on two stretches of road otherwise similar, one with and one without a speed limit, or on the same road before and after a speed limit has been posted, and we then want to know whether the limit has affected the speed of traffic.

6. SIGNIFICANCE

The differences between our samples may be due to the ordinary variations we expect to find in random samples drawn from the same population. On the other hand, the means of the samples may be so different, or the scatter so different, or both at once, that we cannot think of them as drawn from the same population, though we can seldom completely exclude the possibility that they might be.

To test this, we make what are called *tests of significance,* which tell us the probability with which we can expect the observed differences between the means or the scatters to differ from those we would expect to get from the usual error variations.

The difference is said to be *significant*—which term is usually an abbreviation for significantly different from zero—if the probability of its arising from mere error variations is less than some limit called the *level of significance,* or *significance level.* The usual level at which the differences are said to be significant is 'one in twenty' or '0·05' or '5%', which are all ways of saying the same thing. This means that the probability of the difference's occurring by chance is once in twenty trials.

This is not a hard-and-fast rule, but that level has been found from long experience to be the best compromise, and it may be taken as fully tried. It involves the risk that a true hypothesis will be rejected once in twenty trials, but that risk we must take. The level chosen will partly depend on the object of the study. If we were making one on the result of which might depend whether people's licences were to be suspended, it would be reasonable to demand a much more stringent level, say 1% or even 0·1%, the result of suspension having such serious consequences for individuals.

Significance is one of the statistical terms which has a different meaning from that attached to the same word in everyday speech, in which it has definite overtones of importance. In the *Concise Oxford Dictionary* it is defined as 'noteworthy, of considerable importance or effect', but in statistical usage *it has not this meaning*. It just means that the difference would not be expected to have occurred by chance. We can have a large difference which is not significant, and a small one which is. This is important, and should be remembered.

In any report, the level of significance should always be stated. It should not just be said that the difference was significant, but that it was significant at the 5% level, or 1% level, or whatever it was.

7. PERCENTAGES

I sometimes think that the percentage is a personal invention of Satan himself, it is such a fertile source of traps, and nothing is more light-heartedly used to deceive us.

Recently, I heard a person prominent in the road-safety world say that a certain experiment had been highly successful because it had reduced fatal accidents by 200%! I do not think he intended to deceive, but I have no idea what he meant. What he *said* was that, supposing there were twenty deaths a year before the experiment, not only had there been none at all after it—which was not true anyway—but there had also been twenty people a year resurrected. There seems to have been a remarkable failure on the part of the Press in not reporting such unusual events. There cannot be a 200% decrease. A 100% one would have meant the elimination of all deaths.

A recent advertisement in a newspaper read

> ## WORN TYRES
> ## MAKE 3 IN 10
> ## CARS UNSAFE
>
> Tyre failures account for about 28% of breakdowns says the Minister of Transport regarding motorways incidents.

The headlines tell us that 30% of *all* cars have unsafe tyres, while the small type tells us that *about 30% of breakdowns on motorways* are due to tyre failures. These are not the same thing. Only a small proportion of cars break down on motorways, so that it is but 30% of a small proportion of cars which have unsafe tyres. Sweet are the uses of advertisement.

Whenever a percentage is given, it should always be made clear what is meant by it. Thus what does a '200% increase' mean? Have the accidents increased *to* 200% of what they were before, in which case they have doubled, or *by* 200% of what they were before, in which case they have trebled. It is essential to make the matter clear.

8. 'POST HOC, ERGO PROPTER HOC'

This Latin saying refers to a very common type of fallacy. It means, 'because some result followed *after* some measure, argal that result followed *from* that measure'. An example is the kind of thing I have already mentioned, when people say: 'We have done a lot of propaganda, the accidents have fallen, argal our propaganda has been successful.' It may have been, but it also may not have been, we just do not know. The fall may have been due to other things, such as chance variations, or to something else.

Places in the Midlands may have noticed a fall in their accidents in 1960, and have felt tempted to claim that their road-safety measures were taking effect, but what may have really happened was that their area had felt the effect of the opening of the motorway M1 in that year. This event was shown by the RRL to have made a substantial reduction in accidents (RT, p. 418), which could have affected a large surrounding area.

9. 'LIKE WITH LIKE'

A very common method of deception is to compare two different things, hiding the fact that they are different, or relying on people's not noticing the difference. One example is to say that a country such as Sweden has strict legislation on drink and driving and also has fewer accidents than we do, argal strict drink legislation here would reduce our accidents. But Sweden has about the same population and number of motor vehicles as *London,* so it would be expected to have fewer accidents than *Great Britain*. The two countries cannot be compared directly (3.9, p. 23).

Another frequent comparison is between the roads, on which about seven or eight thousand people are killed annually, and the railways, on which in some years no *passengers* are killed. This comparison is misleading on two counts. First of all, the road deaths include everyone killed in any way, even suicide, and deaths at the wheel from a heart attack, while passengers are only a limited section of the people at risk on the railways. There are a number of railway employees killed every year, as well as people killed on platforms and in crossing the lines. During the decade 1951 to 1960 the mean annual number of people killed on the railways was 327. It will be said that this is much smaller than the number killed on the roads, but this is the second way in which the comparison is misleading, because, like the comparison between this country and Sweden, it takes no account of the number of people at risk. There are fewer at risk on the railways than on the roads.

In making such comparisons, we must be sure that the conditions are comparable in the two things compared.

10. 'FIGURES CAN PROVE ANYTHING'

This jibe is made so often that it must be discussed briefly. As I have said, the true statistician never claims proof. It is the propagandists who have given him a bad name by their misuse of figures. If anyone claims that some figures or other 'prove' anything, do not bother with him any more, he either does not know his stuff, or he is wilfully trying to deceive.

But we must have figures. If properly gathered they are facts expressed in numerical form. They must not be rejected because they are inconvenient. If they are rejected, what have we left? Nothing more than dogmatic statement, unsupported by facts, and that is quite valueless, or even harmful, even if it has been made by a bishop or a judge.

3

DEFINITIONS, FACTS AND FIGURES

'I do not pretend to have counted the flies, although they were numerous; and even had I done so, what interest could the number have, save to the statisticians? Now, as these are patient men and foolish, I heartily recommend them to go and count the flies for themselves.'

Hilaire Belloc, The Path to Rome

1. PRELIMINARY

There is so much misunderstanding of the figures, some are suppressed—perhaps deliberately—and others used to deceive, that I must give a few, and also some definitions of terms often misused.

The general reader can get most of the figures he needs from the booklet issued annually by the British Road Federation called *Basic Road Statistics*. It is cheap and easily obtained.

2. DEFINITIONS

There is much confusion in the public mind over the definitions of what are usually misleadingly called 'casualties' in road accidents. An example of this, and also of the failure to compare like with like, was a paper produced at two successive International Road Safety Congresses, one in Salzburg in 1962, and the other in London in 1964. The author claimed that there was an advantage in having the driver's seat in the car on the side nearest the edge of the road. That is, the Continental-type seat should be used in this country with left-hand rule, and a British type on the Continent. He cited as 'proof' of his theory that Sweden, which then used cars with the driver's seat on the left of the car for left-hand rule of the road, had a lower injury rate than this country. At the London Conference Smeed disposed of this by pointing out that Sweden and this country used different definitions of 'injury'. If both countries used the same definition, their injury rates would be much the same, as indeed their death rates were at the time (3.10, p. 26).

It would seem easy to define a death, but when we get down to brass tacks, even this is not as easy as it looks. Do we include someone who dies at the wheel from a heart attack? In this country we do, illogical though it may seem. In the Birmingham

16

Study* it was found that one of the accidents was due to the driver having died at the wheel as a result of a coronary. This was officially returned as a fatal accident. The research team classed it more logically as a non-injury one, because there were no injuries resulting from it. A similar case was reported at an inquest in Dorset.

In another case in Dorset, a driver skidded on a bend which had been the scene of a number of accidents, and the shock brought on a fatal heart attack. The post-mortem found that the heart was in very bad condition, and any shock might have been fatal. This again went down as a fatal accident. This may be less illogical, though it could hardly be said to justify some of the more extravagant descriptions of road deaths. These cases are not frequent, but they illustrate the difficulty of definition.

A much more important difficulty, which does affect the figures materially, is to decide whether we call a death one which occurs at the site of the accident, or some period after it, but due to it. Not all countries adopt the same standard (3.10, p. 27). The Working Party of the United Nations Economic Commission for Europe recommended that the following definitions should be used, and this is done in this country, but not in all:

> (3) '*Deaths*. Persons are reported as killed only if they die from their injuries within thirty days from the accident. *Serious Injury.* An injury for which the person is detained in hospital as an 'in-patient', or any of the following injuries, whether or not he is detained in hospital: fractures, concussion, internal injuries, crushings, severe cuts and lacerations, severe general shock requiring medical treatment. *Slight Injury.* An injury of a minor character such as a sprain, or bruises. Persons who complain of shock, but who sustain no other injury, are only included if they receive, or appear to need, medical treatment.

The last of these definitions shows that the slight injuries are very minor. In spite of the proviso in the last sentence, it may be that

---

* G. M. Mackay, 'Road Accident Research: An Interim Report on the Accident Research Project'. Project Report No. 4, Department of Transportation and Environmental Planning, University of Birmingham. (This will be referred to below as BIR. 4.)

nothing more serious than some dear old lady 'all of a flutter' might be included as a 'slight' injury. This is useful to the traffic engineer, because it increases the size of the sample for his studies, but it can be misleading.

A reportable injury in industry is one which causes death, or prevents a worker, as a result of the injury, earning full wages at the work at which he is employed, for a period of three days. Thus few, if any, of the slight injuries on the road, and possibly even some of the serious injuries, would be recorded at all in industry.

Injuries received in the home, or in games or recreations, are not reported at all, unless they are fatal, and do not appear in any statistics. Their number is probably very large indeed, but we have no means of even guessing at it.

It is usual practice to describe an accident by reference to the most serious injury concerned, irrespective of their number. Thus a *fatal accident*—or *fatality*—would be so called if someone was killed in it. There might or might not be other deaths, or other injuries. This practice will be followed in the rest of the book.

3. 'CASUALTIES'

It is common to refer to all injuries on the roads, even slight ones, as 'casualties'. Even the RRL does so in its publications, though in this case it is writing for specialized readers, who know what is meant, but it confuses the public, and gives an exaggerated picture of the situation—which may sometimes be why it is done.

'Casualty' is associated in the public mind with severe injuries, much more closely approximating to the definition of injury in industry. The *Shorter Oxford Dictionary* actually defines the word as 'a fatal or serious accident', while the *Concise Oxford Dictionary* defines it as 'Accident, mishap, disaster, esp. (plural) list or number of killed, wounded and invalided in a battle, march, war, etc.' The last words perhaps convey the more conventional meaning, and the public mind associates the word with the idea of a fairly serious injury, and absence from work for at least a day or two. The definition of slight injury on the road is hardly compatible with this.

4. 'MAIM' OR 'CRIPPLE'

A still worse practice, which may arise from this misuse of the word casualty, is to describe all those injured on the road, even slightly, as 'maimed' or 'crippled'. This is fantastic nonsense, and can only be done with deliberate intent to mislead, and to exaggerate the problem. It is a gross abuse of words.

5. THE ANNUAL DEATHS IN ACCIDENTS

Figures of the annual road deaths are issued from two sources. The Ministry issue figures from time to time, based on reports sent to them by the police, and publish a summary annually. Figures of all deaths are also issued annually by the Registrars-General for England and Wales, and for Scotland. These figures are summarized in great detail, and so are issued later than the Ministry figures.

There is one important distinction between these. The Registrar-General lists three different categories of what we might call road accidents, dividing them into (*a*) Motor vehicle traffic accidents,

Year	Traffic deaths		Other accidental deaths	Rate per million popn.	
	Motor vehicle	Other road vehicle		m/v traffic	Other accidents
1946	3807	334	10289	96	261
7	3838	336	11229	94	269
8	3506	341	9646	84	227
9	3764	339	9804	89	226
1950	4134	389	10068	97	227
1	4392	306	10407	103	242
2	3971	305	9991	94	231
3	4246	247	10435	99	239
4	4447	258	11919	104	248
5	4908	247	11224	111	255
6	4939	200	11268	113	255
7	4827	220	10954	109	248
8	5366	218	11364	121	255
9	5922	166	11265	132	251
1960	6557	160	11062	145	243
1	6544	144	11171	144	242
2	6230	139	11679	135	248
3	6276	108	12278	135	260

TABLE 1 England and Wales.
Accidental deaths and death rates, 1946–63 (From the Registrar-General's Annual Reviews)

19

(*b*) Motor vehicle non-traffic accidents, and (*c*) Other road vehicle accidents. Those in category (*b*) are in accidents concerning motor vehicles, but not on the public roads. They do not concern us here, and are few in number, under one hundred per year. Category (*c*) takes in deaths in accidents in which no motor vehicle is concerned, involving pedal cycles or horses, either alone or associated with pedestrians. They are few now, but have been important in the past, amounting to 10% of the total number of road deaths, and in 1935 they amounted to over 12% of all deaths on the road. This figure is included in the Ministry road deaths, but is not separated out, and few people even know that it exists. Figures showing these are in Table 1.

The table shows figures for England and Wales only, so as to be comparable with a later table. It also includes the annual deaths in other types of accident.

6. THE HOURLY DISTRIBUTION OF ACCIDENTS

Table 2 shows the hours at which people were killed over the Christmas weekend of 1963. It was originally published by the RRL* but I have rearranged it so as to make the distribution of the accidents clearer. The small hours of Christmas Day are really part of Christmas Eve.

7. TRAVEL ACCIDENTS BEFORE MOTORING

It is often said that travel accidents have only become a serious problem with the introduction of the motor vehicle, and conclusions are drawn from this 'fact', so figures setting out the real situation are of interest and importance.

We cannot have had motor vehicle accidents before motors, but these have replaced other forms of transport, and extended the amount of travel, so it is reasonable to compare modern road accidents with those which occurred in pre-motor days in those types of travel which would now be done by motor. Thus some of the railway accidents, all the accidents in horse transport, and many drownings a century ago, would be comparable with modern road accidents.

An interesting historical comparison is that some of our not very

---

* 'Fatal Road Accidents at Christmas 1963', Road Research Technical Paper No. 72, DSIR Road Research Laboratory. London: HMSO.

Hour starting	Date	No. killed	Date	No. killed	Date	No. killed	Date	No. killed	Total
5·00	23rd		24th		25th		26th		
6·00		1							1
7·00		1		1		1			3
8·00		3		1					4
9·00		1							1
10·00								1	1
11·00		2				2			4
12·00		1		1				3	5
13·00				2		4		2	8
14·00		1		1		2			4
15·00		1		7		1		1	10
16·00		1		5		3		1	10
17·00		4		8		1		2	15
18·00		2		5				1	8
19·00		1		5		1		3	10
20·00		2		2		1		3	8
21·00		1		1				1	3
22·00		4		4		1			9
23·00		2		4		1		3	10
0·00	24th		25th	6	26th	1	27th		7
1·00				2					2
2·00				3					3
3·00				5				1	6
4·00				1					1
Total		28		64		19		22	133

TABLE 2 England and Wales.
Times at which people were killed, Christmas 1963

numerous monarchs since the Conquest died as a result of travel injuries: William I, whose horse fell at Mantes in France; William III, whose horse fell in Kensington Park; and Alexander III of Scotland, who was killed by a fall from his horse on a journey in 1286. There are many references to travel accidents in literature, and they caused deaths long before the days of the motor.

A recent paper has published figures extracted from the early Registrar-General's Reviews and I have made up Table 3 partly from it and partly from the recent Registrar-General's Reviews.

The rate per million of population is given instead of the absolute numbers because it would obviously be unrealistic not to do this. I have also included drowning because there was a much greater use of water transport a century ago than there is now, both inland on rivers and canals, and in coastwise shipping.

The use of coastwise shipping for transport is mentioned in Boswell and Jane Austen, both in contexts in which the corresponding journeys would now be done by road. This is, of course, earlier than 1863, but in *The Last Chronicle of Barset,* set about that year, Trollope mentioned that brickworks were situated at Hoggle End, many miles from any railway, because a canal could take the bricks to London and Bristol. Smaller harbours, once busy, but now hardly used, are common on the coasts.

The table shows that travel accidents may even have been more frequent a century ago than they are now, at least for men. The slight increase in those for females is probably due to much greater travel by the modern woman.

(a) Males

Type of accident \ Years	1863–70	1891–1900	1931–1938	1963
Railway	71	59	20	9
Road	124	90	235	204
Drowning	214	151	58	30
	409	300	313	243

(b) Females

Railway	5	4	2	1
Road	19	17	76	74
Drowning	37	27	12	7
	61	48	90	82

Note: The reason for including drowning is discussed in the text

From: Deaths by violence 1837–1937. Greenwood Martin & Russel. Journal Roy Stat. Soc. 1941 104(2) and recent Registrar-General's Statistical Reviews.

TABLE 3 England and Wales.
Death rates in travel accidents, per million of population

8. ACCIDENT RATES IN GREAT BRITAIN

The RRL has calculated the accident rates for various types of road in this country, the mileage being estimated for this from a traffic census which is being carried on continuously by recording counters permanently installed at fifty points covering the country, chosen by a random sampling process. I have made up Table 4 partly from their table in RS, and partly from other information.

	Shopping centres	8 − 13
	Residential roads	4 − 7
	Roads not built-up, but with much traffic	4 − 7
Great Britain	Rural roads with light traffic	$1\frac{1}{2}-2\frac{1}{2}$
	A 38. Gloucester Bristol. Heavy traffic, two-lane 1958	2·6
	" " " " " all three-lane 1965	1·3
	Dual carriageways, Lancashire	1·4
	Motorway M I (1964)	0·6
	Doncaster Bypass Motorway AI.(M),1962	0·5
	Pennsylvania Turnpike (Motorway) U.S.A. 1966	0·9

TABLE 4 Great Britain.
Injury accident rates on various types of road

These figures should be treated with some reserve. They are only approximate, but make a rough comparison.

I have also made up Table 5 to show the *comparative* rates for different types of road-user, calculating them from the figures of accidents per vehicle mile given in the Ministry publication *Road Accidents 1965*. For this table, I have divided the rate for the different types by that for private cars, so making the latter arbitrarily equal to 1, so all the rates are proportional to private cars.

9. INTERNATIONAL COMPARISONS

Comparisons are often made between accidents in this country and those in others, needless to say always to our disparagement. These are usually invalidated by failure to compare like with like.

In most countries, road-accident deaths appear to be approximately related to the population and to the number of

Road-user	Type of accident		
	All injury	Serious injury	Fatal
Mopeds	2·6	2·8	1·3
Motor-scooters	6·2	6·4	3·1
Motor-cycles	6·3	8·0	5·8
Cars and taxis	1·0	1·0	1·0
Goods vehicles. Under $1\frac{1}{2}$ tons. u.w.	1·1	1·1	1·0
" " Over " "	0·7	0·8	1·7
Public service vehicles	2·5	1·8	2·4
Pedal cycles	2·5	2·1	1·7

TABLE 5 Great Britain
Relative accident rates for different types of road-user, 1965

motor vehicles combined. Smeed, at the RRL, worked out an approximate formula connecting the three, using the figures in twenty countries for 1938 (RS). His equation is:

$$D = 300 \ (np^2)^{1/3} \ ... \ (\text{equ. } 1)$$

In this D is the annual number of road deaths, n is the number of registered motor vehicles in the country, and p the population, both expressed in millions. In 1938, the predicted number of deaths from the formula differed from the actual number by a margin of 15 % in half of the twenty countries, while for all but one of the rest the predicted deaths were within 40% of the actual number. For figures like this, these differences are reasonable, and the formula may be accepted as giving a rough guide to the expected number of deaths annually in a country.

The discussion on this formula in RS expected that it would fit better as road conditions, and the experience of road-users, both improve.

In July 1965, the RRL issued Lab. Note No. LN/887/JS giving more up-to-date statistics for twenty-six countries, so I tested their forecast by comparing the figures for 1961—which was the latest year for which complete figures were given—with the formula. It did not fit the figures as well as it had in 1938. For that year, only one country's actual figure exceeded prediction by 40%, while for

1961 three countries had double the number expected. The forecast has apparently not been fulfilled.

When doing this, I noticed that countries with left-hand rule of the road seemed to be consistently below prediction, except for Australia and South Africa, though these did not greatly exceed it. The two latter countries, however, are relatively lightly populated for their area, and there is reason to think that such countries would be expected to have a high death rate (4.3, p. 34). The idea that the rule of the road might have an effect on deaths is new, and needed more study.

I therefore worked out a new formula, using only right-hand rule countries, and got the following expression:

$$D = 360 \ (np^2)^{1/3} \ ... \ \text{(equ. 2)}$$

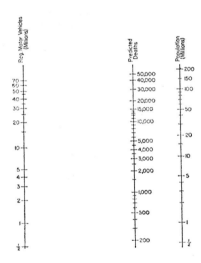

FIGURE 1 Nomogram for calculating the predicted annual deaths in a country from the Modified Smeed formula

This is exactly similar in principle to Smeed's, except for the multiplying constant of 360 instead of the 300 in the formula. I shall call it the 'Modified Smeed' formula. It fits the later figures much better than the original one.

The solution of this equation is tedious, involving the use of logarithms, but the chart of Figure 1 enables it to be done quite nearly enough. To use it, lay a straight edge or piece of black thread across the chart, putting one end against the number of motor vehicles on the left-hand line, and the other for population on the right-hand line, when the predicted number of annual deaths can be read off on the middle line.

The sample for left-hand rule of the road countries is a small one, only five in all, excluding Australia and South Africa for the reasons given above. To increase it, I used Great Britain for two years, 1961 and 1964, and Sweden for two years also, 1961 and 1963. I then found that the formula:

$$D = 250 \, (np^2)^{1/3} \dots \text{(equ. 3)}$$

fitted the figures very well indeed. Great Britain, Sweden and New Zealand were all within 5% of prediction, Eire only 6% above, and Northern Ireland was 12% below. This is a very good agreement. Here, again, the only difference from Smeed is in the factor of 250 instead of 300. I shall call it the 'left-hand formula'.

It thus seems possible that left-hand rule of the road countries have about two-thirds of the annual deaths that right-hand rule ones have. Figure 1 can be used for left-hand rule countries by taking two-thirds of the figure given on the middle line.

In the—possibly sanguine—hope of checking some of the wilder comparisons, I give in Table 6 two tables, (a) for seventeen right-hand rule countries showing predicted and actual figures worked out from the Modified Smeed Formula, and (b) for five left-hand rule countries, showing the predicted figures from the Modified Smeed and from the left-hand formula. Australia is included for comparison. The table (b) shows how well the left-hand formula agrees.

10. DIFFERENCES IN REPORTING DEATHS

A source of some confusion in the reported figures is that some

(a) Right−hand rule of road countries Predicted deaths from "Modified Smeed"formula $D = 360 \, (np^2)^{1/3}$			
Country	Predicted	Actual	$\frac{Actual}{Predicted}$
Austria	1400	1640	1·17
Belgium (adjusted*)	1850	2160	1·85
Canada	4270	3426	0·80
Denmark	894	841	0·94
France (adjusted*)	10,470	10,500	1·00
Finland	714	786	1·10
Western Germany	10,640	14,220	1·34
Italy (adjusted*)	9030	18,000	1·99
Luxembourg	70	76	1·07
Netherlands	2340	1997	0·85
Norway	690	365	0·53
Poland	3740	2525	0·67
Portugal (adjusted*)	985	1476	1·50
Spain (adjusted*)	3710	2348	0·63
Switzerland	1090	1381	1·27
Turkey	1770	1822	1·03
U.S.A.	47,300	38,091	0·80

(b) Left−hand rule of road countries			Predicted from "Modified Smeed"		Predicted from "left−hand formula" $D = 250 \, (np^2)^{1/3}$	
Country		Actual	Predicted	$\frac{Actual}{Predicted}$	Predicted	$\frac{Actual}{Predicted}$
Australia	1961	2542	2420	1·05	1730	1·47
Eire	1961	332	450	0·74	313	1·06
Great Britain	1961	6908	10,201	0·68	7050	0·98
Great Britain	1964	7820	11,140	0·70	7720	1·01
Northern Ireland	1961	169	280	0·61	193	0·88
Sweden	1961	1083	1570	0·69	1090	1·00
Sweden	1963	1121	1650	0·68	1140	0·98

*See 3.10 and Table 8 for adjustments

TABLE 6 International comparisons of deaths for 1961

countries do not use the Working Party definition of a death (3.2, p. 17). Belgium, Italy and Portugal only report one as such if it occurs at the scene of the accident, otherwise it is reported as injury; Spain reports a death if it occurs within twenty-four hours after the accident, France if within three days, and the U.S.A. if death results within a year of the accident. This means that their returns of deaths are not strictly comparable with those given by the countries which use the Working Party definitions. Allowance can be made for this by multiplying the reported figures by the factors given in Table 7 (RS).

Belgium, Italy, Portugal	multiply by		2·00
Spain	„	„	1·30
France	„	„	1·15
U.S.A.	„	„	0·97
Italy (since 1 January 1964)	„	„	1·07

TABLE 7 Corrections to published figures of deaths

In computing the Modified Smeed formula I used these factors, except for the U.S.A. In 1964 Italy changed the method of reporting by counting a death as one occurring within seven days of the accident, without much change in the published figures, which perhaps illustrates the unreliability of such figures.

There are other possible sources of inaccuracy in the published figures which we cannot include owing to lack of information. Some countries do not count mopeds as motor vehicles, and others do. As these are mechanically propelled it might be argued that they should be included. They are in this country, but their number is small.

No country says whether or not it includes 'Other road vehicle' (3.5, p. 19) deaths in its published figures. When we were less motorized in Great Britain, they amounted to about 10% of the deaths, so that in a country like Italy, which seems to have a large number of pedal cycles, they might amount to between 1,000 and 1,500 deaths per year, which would decidedly affect the fit of the formulae. It would obviously be misleading to include deaths in which no motor vehicle was involved in any comparison associating deaths and the number of motor vehicles.

II. COMPARISONS BETWEEN STATES IN THE U.S.A.

A similar comparison has been made for the states of the U.S.A. by two statisticians from the American Automobile Association. * They found that a formula could be worked out which would predict the annual death rate per vehicle mile—*not as in the Smeed formula the number of deaths*—in the various states of the Union. This formula is more detailed than Smeed's because more uniform information is available in the U.S.A. than in Europe.

They took into account thirty factors which it was thought might affect the death rate. Among these were included the annual consumption of wine, of spirits and of malt beverages—taken individually—the amount spent on road maintenance, the minimum temperature, certain of the legal measures such as the amount spent on police, the number of police per 100,000 inhabitants, the follow-up programme on dangerous drivers, the quality of driver testing, and so on.

The thirty factors were finally reduced to six on elimination of those which were found to have small or negligible effect. The final six were:

(*a*) The percentage of the total state highway mileage that is rural.

(*b*) The per cent increase in motor vehicle registration.

(*c*) The extent of motor vehicle inspection.

(*d*) The percentage of state-administered highway that is surfaced.

(*e*) The average yearly minimum temperature.

(*f*) The income per capita.

These are placed in descending order of importance. These six accounted for 70% of the variations in the rate.

In 1952 the agreement with this formula was good. The states which differed most from prediction were Maine, with an actual rate two-thirds of predicted, and Utah in which the actual rate was one and one-third times prediction. The State with the lowest rates are the more densely populated Eastern States, the lowest being

---

* Earl Allgaier and Sam Yaksich, 'Factors Relating to Traffic Death Rates'. Research Report No. 55. Washington: American Automobile Association.

29

Rhode Island, and the next lowest Connecticut. The highest was South Carolina, with Nevada next highest.

12. COMPARISONS BETWEEN RATES PER VEHICLE MILE IN GREAT BRITAIN AND THE U.S.A.

It is frequently said that our death rate per vehicle mile compares very unfavourably with that in the U.S.A. Our pedestrian rate compares unfavourably, but the rest are similar, though pedal cycles are rare in the U.S.A. These rates are shown in Table 8.*

Type of road-user		Great Britain	U.S.A.
Pedestrian		3·8	1·1
Pedal-cyclists		1·1	0·1
Others	Drivers	1·1 ⎫	
	Motor-cyclists & passengers	2·5 ⎬ 4·9	4·3
	Other passengers	1·3 ⎭	
Total		9·8	5·5

TABLE 8 Fatalities per hundred million vehicle miles In Great Britain and the U.S.A., 1959

13. AGE AND ACCIDENTS

It is often suggested that older drivers are likely to have more accidents. Figure 2 shows the percentage of licensed drivers *involved*—though not necessarily to blame—in accidents by age in the state of Connecticut, U.S.A., I have calculated the figures from *Facts 1959* published by the State Department of Motor Vehicles, and have drawn a smooth curve through the calculated figures. The points come very close to the curve. The age with least drivers involved will be seen to be 84. The sample for that age was small, but not negligible, 428 drivers with 4 involved in accidents. The older drivers probably do smaller mileages than younger ones, though this should naturally be taken into consideration when deciding whether the old should be allowed to drive.

Figure 3 shows the estimated relative rates of drivers involved per

* From Starks, Garwood, Jeffcoate and Smeed, 'Researeh into Road Traffic Accidents'. Paper presented to the World Traffic Engineering Conference, Nice, 1960.

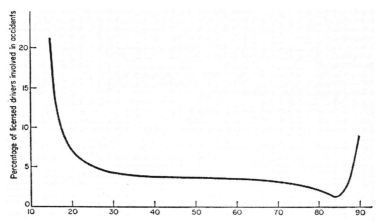

FIGURE 2 Connecticut, U.S.A.
Percentage of licensed drivers involved in accidents by year of age

vehicle mile in Great Britain.* In this diagram, the mean rate is taken as 1·0, so the curve shows each age relative to the mean. The curve has been rounded off from groups given in the original paper, so should not be taken as exact.

A recent study of driver involvement by age in the State of Washington, U.S.A., points rather the same way (TQ, October 1967).

14. THE STOPPING DISTANCE

A table of stopping distances is given on the back cover of the Highway Code. These are rather on the short side, being based on optimistic figures of a driver reaction time of about two-thirds of a second, with the car, its tyres and the road all in excellent condition. To make better allowance for practical conditions, *Civil Engineering Reference Book*† gives a simplified formula for this distance:

$$S = \frac{V^2}{6} + 1 \cdot 5V$$

---

* This curve is plotted from figures given by J. M. Munden, 'The Accident Rates of Car Drivers by Age'. London: *International Road Safety and Traffic Review*, Vol. XIV, No. 1.

† *Civil Engineering Reference Book*, ed. Probst and Comrie. Section: 'Highways', J. J. Leeming. London: Butterworth & Co. (Publishers) Ltd 1951.

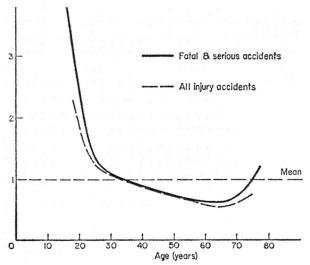

FIGURE 3 Great Britain. Estimated relative involvement rates per hundred million vehicle miles by age of driver

Speed (Mile/h)	Stopping distances (feet)	
	CERB Formula	Highway Code
20	97	40
30	195	75
40	327	120
50	482	175
60	690	240

TABLE 9 Stopping distance for various speeds

in which *S* is the stopping distance in feet and *V* is the speed in mile/h.

This would give distances according to Table 9, in which table those given in the Highway Code are included for comparison.

The distances according to the CERB formula are perhaps rather more realistic than the Code's, especially in poor weather, and if a pedestrian were to step out smartly that distance in front of a car doing the speed shown, a potential accident situation would arise.

32

4

THE PROBLEM

'It isn't that they can't see the solution. It is that they can't see the problem.'

G. K. Chesterton, 'The Point of a Pin' from
The Scandal of Father Brown

1. 'TRANSPORTATION IS CIVILIZATION'

This saying, a quotation from the story 'As Easy as ABC' from *A Diversity of Creatures* by Rudyard Kipling, sums up a very profound truth. Without transport, and the movement of goods and people, there can be no civilization and culture, in places even no life at all. The increase in the standard of living in many parts of the world in recent years has been almost entirely due to the great strides made in transport, especially by the introduction of the motor vehicle with its flexibility and ability to get into places otherwise inaccessible, even by railways.

The motor has made a difference to life in many ways. Travel has become more general, and people can get about more easily than they could when there were only railways, access to which was by horsed vehicles. In those days people of wealth and leisure could travel, but the workers, including professional people under that title, could only do so on a very limited scale. They could not wander all over Europe as they do now. The change the motorcar has made for the worker, even in a few years, was mentioned by Harold Macmillan, the former Premier, in an interview on BBC television.

(4) 'I think the chief change, particularly in the industrial areas has been mobility ... That is a new thing—on the moors and the hills and in the dales. Before, they would just stay at home, and there was no amusement but football and drink.' (L, 8.9.66.)

He was speaking about the industrial workers on Tees-side. This mobility, with the ability to distribute goods easily and cheaply, has been the benefit the motor vehicle has conferred on us.

2. DANGERS IN TRAVEL

There has never been a time when travel was not dangerous. St Paul mentions it in 2 Corinthians, 11. Risk exists as soon as any object starts to move relative to its surroundings. The dangers about which St Paul writes are those from rivers and robbers, while now we have them from the impact of the vehicles. Modern conditions have changed the type of danger, but whether they have increased or decreased the probability of accident is a matter of guesswork; we do not know. Many people say that it has enormously increased, even that it has started, with the motor vehicle.

Norman* puts it thus:

> (5) 'The problem of road traffic accidents on a large scale has arisen for the first time in the present century. All other epidemics throughout history have been due to the onslaught of agencies external to man, principally the protozoa, bacteria and viruses; but road accidents are due to man himself. A terrible penalty of mortality has already been paid as the cost of integrating the motor vehicle into modern life. The motor vehicle has developed from somewhat primitive beginnings to a stage at which a set of armchairs, fully enclosed in a mass of metal, often weighing a ton or more, can be hurled from a standstill to fifty or sixty miles an hour or more in a matter of seconds, by the lightest touch of a couple of levers, and can attain far higher speeds in smoothness and comfort. *All this occurs on roads that were mostly built for horse traffic:* it is not surprising that an accident problem has arisen.' [My italics, J.J.L.]

This is a little highly coloured, and its accuracy is debatable on several grounds. As Table 3 (p. 22) shows, the statement in the first sentence is not true. It could also be argued that the plagues of the Middle Ages, such as the Black Death, were due to man himself, by his crowding into insanitary cities, and neglecting hygiene, nevertheless the quotation does illustrate a very generally held opinion.

3. INCIDENTAL DEATHS

By an *incidental death* I mean one which is in some way associated with transport, or perhaps more often with its absence, but is not directly due to the instrument of transport itself.

---

* L. G. Norman, 'Road Traffic Accidents. Epidemiology, Control and Prevention'. Public Health Paper No. 12. Geneva: World Health Organization, 1962.

34

An example was given in a recent BBC television programme on a country in Africa. Pictures were shown of a young woman, said to be of some intellectual attainments, who had died from a disease which could easily have been treated in hospital, but she lived so far away, with limited means of transport, that she could not be got to hospital in time to save her life.

A similar case, fortunately not resulting in death, is of some interest, because it also exemplifies the propagandist methods. Some years ago it was reported in the Press that Sweden had few deaths over the Christmas weekend, while we had many. Sweden has strict laws about drink and driving, argal, it was said, those laws kept the accidents down, argal we should have those laws. But I had a letter from friends living in Central Sweden, telling me that they had had a very heavy snowfall over the Christmas weekend, and that a friend staying with them had had a severe heart attack and had nearly died because the ambulance was unable to get him to hospital. If he had died, this could be called an incidental death.

The fall in the deaths in Sweden that weekend may have been due to the snow preventing travel, and to have had nothing to do with the drink laws. We were not told anything about the snowfall, and also of the fact that Christmas is not celebrated to the same extent in Sweden as it is here.

In the U.S.A. the states with the highest death rates from road accidents are the Middle Western states, while the more populated eastern states have lower rates. As Moynihan puts it, if you have an accident in Washington D.C., which has the lowest rate, you will not be likely to be more than fifteen blocks from a hospital, while in Colorado you may be 150 miles. In some degree, then, the deaths in the Western states are partly incidental, due to the difficulty of getting the injured to hospital because of the vast distances. There has recently been discussion of this both in France and in this country, and it has been said that many lives could be saved if there were quicker facilities for dealing with the injured.

The motor must have very much reduced the incidental deaths in such ways as making it easier for doctors to visit their patients, in conveying those patients to hospital more quickly and comfortably, in enabling fire engines to reach fires quicker, and possibly in other ways, such as its having eliminated the filth due to horses in the streets of the cities. I am as old as the motor vehicle, and I can still remember the horrible mess in the London streets, and in the mews at the back of the big houses. This must have caused much fly-borne disease.

The horses used for transport and farm work needed large areas for grazing, which areas are now used for growing food for humans, because the horses have been replaced by motors.

4. THE PROBLEM

Is there a new problem in the sense of an enormous increase in deaths due to the use of motor vehicles? The balance of probability is that there is not. We have about 500,000 deaths per year, and about 8,000 of these are road deaths. If we abolished the motor vehicle completely, on 1 January 1970, would the number of deaths that year fall to 492,000, assuming that we were able to make alternative arrangements for transport? Almost certainly not. It is far more probable that they would increase. The incidental deaths would probably rise, and Table 3 (p. 22) shows that travel deaths might increase also.

That does not mean that we have not a problem to solve, merely that the problem is not the same as the one that we pretend to be trying to solve. The hint is given in the sentence of Norman's that I have italicized in Quotation 5 (p. 34). There is little reason to doubt that we could very materially reduce the number of deaths per year, but because we are not trying to solve the real problem, we are not saving these lives.

The heart of the matter is that Norman's words ought to read:

(5a) A terrible penalty of mortality has already been paid as the cost of *allowing prejudice and ignorance to prevent* our integrating the motor vehicle into modern life. [The words in italics are my addition.]

The real problem is, then, that we have a new means of transport which has already conferred great benefits on mankind, and could confer more if we allowed it to do so, but we are so wedded to ancient prejudices and old-fashioned ways that we are not even

36

trying to study the problem, let alone to solve it. It is taken for granted that we know all there is to know about it, so that no attempt is made to find out the answers to the real questions. We do not even realize what these questions are.

5

CAUSATION AND THE INQUIRY INTO ACCIDENTS

'Oh Thou, who didst with Pitfall and with Gin
Beset the Road I was to wander in,
Thou wilt not with predestination round
Enmesh me, and impute my fall to Sin?'

Rubaiyat of Omar Khayyam of Nishapur.
Trans. Edward Fitzgerald

1. BENNETT'S THEORY

In beginning to consider the problem, we must first ask why accidents happen. At present they are attributed to human error, to wilful and deliberate human error at that, and it is further assumed that the error is solely on the part of the driver of the motor vehicle. The fall is always imputed to sin.

But, thirty years ago, Bennett pointed out that this is one-sided. He argued that we must look deeper, and try to find out why the human erred. He did not mean that human error is not present, he expressly said that it is. His argument was that the error itself may have some cause external to the driver.

To illustrate this point, I will take an example which has occurred many times in my own experience. I shall discuss it in detail below, but use it here to illustrate Bennett's line of thought. There is a bend on a road which a certain man uses frequently, so that he knows at what speed to take it. Then its surface polishes suddenly, and the next time he takes it he skids and has an accident. One could call it bad driving, but can one claim that the surface was nothing at all to do with his accident?

Here, again, I am not discussing the question of blame. Neither was Bennett. The point is HOW COULD THAT ACCIDENT HAVE BEEN PREVENTED? Just that, and nothing more, but I ask the reader to face the fact that *this is a complete revolution in thought on the matter.*

I would go further than Bennett, and say that human error is *always* present in an accident, though this is not necessarily on the part of the driver. If a tree falls on a car, it could be said that there was human error. Someone should have seen that the tree was unsafe and done something about it.

Bennett's argument was that we should seek the reasons behind the human error. If we do this, we can then go on to find out what is the best way of eliminating it. At present, we first look for—and find!—some fault or other on the part of the driver, which may or may not have been relevant to the accident, and then—full stop. The inquiry ends there, with his prosecution and punishment. But the traffic engineer argues that this punishment may not be the best way of stopping future accidents of the same type. *It is often an excellent way of ensuring that more happen.* This would certainly be so in the case of the slippery bend I have mentioned above. There the only way of preventing more accidents is to treat the surface, an easy and cheap operation. The prosecution may be far more likely to prevent the engineer finding out that the surface is slippery, and so be the means of causing more accidents.

The traffic engineer studies the accident as far as he is allowed. He looks into all its circumstances, and if some change in any one of these could have been expected to have altered or prevented the accident, he would then call this circumstance a *causal factor,* or *factor* for short. We drop the use of the word 'cause'. It is misleading and prejudices the situation. It also follows that we can seldom attribute the accident to a single factor. The official statements very often show only one 'cause' for each accident, and one sees lists of 'causes' published, each one with its percentage of occurrence shown against it, and all these percentages adding neatly up to 100. More of Hamlet's miching mallecho. *If any report includes such a list, it should go straight into the waste-paper basket.* It is misleading nonsense.

We now shift our priority from the prosecution of the driver to the elimination of the factor which is the easiest and cheapest to eliminate. At present we pretend to remove human error on the part of the driver by legal action, and all other measures have a low priority, if any. They are called 'fringe measures'. But here we have extended the inquiry. We ask: 'Why did that man skid?' We do not just say 'bad driving', and leave it at that.

2. AN ACCIDENT CONSIDERED

I will now list the factors in an actual incident, to illustrate the point. I have chosen it because it includes almost all the usual ones.

Two men left a public house on the advice of the landlord, who thought that, although they were not actually drunk, they had had enough. He did not think the driver incapable of driving. They went on northwards three or four miles, and came to a crossroads called Warmwell Cross. There the driver shot straight across, paying no attention to a Halt sign. A lorry, passing from east to west, collided with their car, and both men were killed.

This would normally be dismissed out of hand as a simple affair, due to drink. I shall deal with the incident in detail below (6.11, p. 64) and for the moment say that it was by no means as simple as that. The factors which study showed to exist were:

(*a*) Chance.
(*b*) Human error.
(*c*) Deception in the road layout.
(*d*) The law:
    (i)   in preventing and delaying my finding out the deception in the road layout,
    (ii) in the design of the Halt sign,
    (iii) in the Halt sign encouraging and authorizing the driver on the main road to barge ahead.
(*e*) Drink.

Headings *a* to *d* cover most of the main types of factor, and to complete the list we must add that of the machine, which was not present here. Almost all factors in accidents will be variants of these five main types, though all are not necessarily present in every accident.

In setting out the factors in this list, I have put them in descending order of the confidence we feel that they were present in that particular incident. There is always an element of conjecture in all these studies. In this case, we can be almost 100% confident that the first four were present, down to *d*(i) inclusive. A roundabout which was built there not long after this incident has had no fatal accidents, and few of any sort in over four years after its completion (Table 14, p. 68), so we can reasonably expect that if it had been there at the date of the accident, the victims would have passed on their way, drink or no drink.

Factor *e,* that of drink, is the one which we can be least confident was present. The drink may have made the driver fall into the trap. On the other hand, he might have fallen into it if he had not been drinking. That is anybody's guess. We have no means of knowing.

I must again remind the reader that I am not attributing blame. I am saying that if factors *a* to *d*(i) had been different, the accident might not have happened. If the roundabout had been there, the car might have gone round it, and the two men would most probably not have been killed. That is all.

3. THE PROPER OBJECT OF THE INQUIRY INTO ACCIDENTS

Summarizing what has gone before, the traffic engineer, when he studies an accident, tries to find out all the factors present, without imputing blame to anyone, and the criterion for something's being a factor is that its being different would have altered or prevented the accident. His next step is to study which of the factors would be the easiest and cheapest to eliminate to prevent further similar incidents. This may be called a cold-blooded approach, but, when it is considered objectively, it is practical and reasonable, which, indeed, is why it is the present practice in railway and air accidents. It goes back over a century on the railways, on which the inquiries have always been wholly devoted towards finding out how to stop further accidents, and not towards punishing individuals.

The most extraordinary feature of the road accident inquiry is that this is *not* done, and that when it was suggested by Bennett thirty years ago, his proposal was received with scorn.

4. THE FACTOR OF CHANCE

This is put in here because, although it is important, it hardly warrants a chapter to itself. The presence of chance makes the use of statistical methods appropriate to the study, and it has some practical applications in the design of the civil engineering measures we use.

The simplest example of its occurrence is that very common type of accident, a collision at a crossroads, such as that at Warmwell Cross, already discussed. Figure 4 is a generalized and diagrammatic plan of a crossroads—a minor road intersecting a dual carriageway—which is taken so as to simplify the problem. We will imagine a stream of traffic passing along the near carriageway in a random manner.

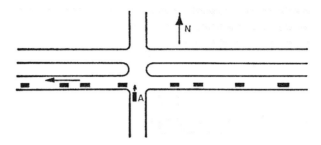

FIGURE 4 Diagrammatic plan of a crossroads

It has been observed that the spacing of traffic, when it is free to move as it will and has reasonable freedom to overtake, will be distributed along the road according to what is called the Poisson distribution, which governs cases in which the probability of an event occurring is small, but the number of times it could occur is very large. This means that the individual vehicles composing the traffic stream will have gaps of varying length between them, and will not be evenly spaced along the road. Some of the gaps will be long, and some short.

Now imagine a car A, on Figure 4, travelling northwards, to drive straight across the near carriageway without stopping, as the car did at Warmwell Cross. If the main-road traffic is light, it is very likely that no collision will occur, because the probability of long gaps in the main-road traffic is also high, so A will probably find one. But collisions will occasionally occur, and that is what happened at Warmwell Cross. The long shot came off—with fatal results. We had actually observed a large number of cars drive across without any collision. This was one of the exceptions. As the traffic on the main road increases, so will the probability of collision increase if a car did as A was imagined to do.

Other cases of similar type will also occur, such as a driver overtaking on a blind bend. If he finds one of the gaps he gets away with it. If not, there is an accident.

There is also some further element of chance in the results of an accident, that is, whether it is fatal on the one hand, or non-injury on the other. I have mentioned an extreme case in Dorset when a skid which might not in the ordinary way have resulted in more than minor damage was fatal, because the driver's heart was in bad condition.

It also follows—and although this is not strictly relevant to the matter of chance, this may be the best place to mention it—that the crossroads situation presents a problem to the most careful driver. If there is any important volume of traffic on the main road, crossing it presents a nice problem in relative speeds which he has little time to solve, and, as the volume increases, this problem becomes more and more difficult, until finally it becomes impossible of solution and he cannot cross safely. It is perhaps hardly surprising that a few drivers fail to solve the problem.

6

THE EFFECT OF ROAD IMPROVEMENTS

'You can't stop all accidents by road improvements.'
Popular saying; also the stock excuse made by all Ministers of Transport

1. BEFORE-AND-AFTER STUDIES

Before discussing the effects of changes in road conditions, I must explain how we estimate the results. That is done by means of *before-and-after* studies. In these, the actual number of accidents which occur at some site after a change has been made in road conditions are compared with the number which would have been expected to have taken place there if no work had been done.

This figure is derived by making the reasonable assumption that the accidents at the site would have changed at the same rate as those in a surrounding—or in some way comparable—area, which should also be large compared with the site. In my own studies, the results of which are given here, I usually used the whole county in which the site was situated. Then the number of accidents in this area after the change, divided by the number before it, both for the corresponding periods, gives us a figure called the *Control*.

The length of the periods for which the accidents are compared is a matter of compromise. If it is made too long there is the possibility that other changes than those at the site might affect the situation, while if it is made too short, the normal chance variations always present in such figures might have too much influence. Three years is often thought to be the best compromise period, and most of the figures I have given here are based on this. The after period could be less provided the control period corresponds.

The object of the study is to compare the accidents at the original unaltered site with those on the new work fully and completely altered to its final form. Any accidents taking place at the site during construction would be disregarded.

The comparison of single small sites in this way is not very useful because chance variations would play too large a part. I therefore aimed at getting the largest possible number of sites where the same kind of work had been done, and those spread as widely as possible all over the country. These were then combined by a statistical analysis due to Tanner at the RRL. This estimates the mean proportional variation in the number of accidents over the whole of the sites in the sample and tests whether the effect can be thought of as consistent among them, and also whether the change is significant. The use of a large number of sites also helps to make the effect of the error variations cancel out.

The figures available for some of the types of work did enable me to analyse the fatal and serious accidents, taken together, as well as those associated with all injuries, but this was not always possible. In a few cases, I was even able to analyse fatals only. That is, *the number of fatal accidents, not the number of deaths*. This tests the common theory that while some forms of road improvement may reduce minor accidents, they will increase the serious ones by speeding up the traffic. If this is true, it might also follow that speed limits might have the reverse effect of making accidents less serious by reducing the speed of traffic.

The process of using a control as described above could introduce an inaccuracy if the change at the site was large in proportion to the total number of accidents in the control area, and if the control included the site. This could have happened in a study of the effect of one-way streets in the Borough of Torquay for which the Borough Engineer kindly supplied me with figures. The system affected such a high proportion of the streets in the town that, if it did have any effect on the accidents, the conclusion from the study would have been biased if the total number of accidents in the town itself had been used as a control, so I used the County of Devon instead.

It might be thought that the volume of traffic would make a better control than the number of accidents. There are two difficulties in this. First of all, we very often do not know the changes in traffic at the sites studied. There are not traffic counters all over the place, and estimates made from counts some way from the site might be very unreliable. In the second place, we do not know enough about the relation between changes in traffic volume and the number of accidents. It seems improbable that accidents double if the traffic doubles. It is sometimes thought that they may go up in proportion to the square root of the traffic increase, so that if the traffic doubled the accidents would rise by about 41%. This is by no means established, so the present method seems to be the best and most reliable one with our present information.

There is some evidence from motorways that the accident rate per vehicle mile *falls* with increasing traffic density up to a certain point, and it may rise again after reaching that point. If this is so, it would add a further complication if the traffic volume was used as a control.

2. THE TABLE

The results obtained from a number of analyses are set out in Table 10. To get them I have used figures sent me by a number of County Surveyors in Great Britain and Northern Ireland specially for this book, and combined them with similar ones sent me for a paper presented to the Third Scientific Meeting of the British Academy for Forensic Sciences in 1962.*

The layout of the table should be clear. The columns and lines have been numbered for easy reference in the text.

The figures given in columns 4, 6, and 8 may need some

Column	1	2	3	4	5	
		No. of			Ratio of ac	
Line	No. of counties	sites in sample	Type of change	All injury accidents		
				Ratio	Significance	
	(a)	Civil	engineering works			
1	4	5	Motorways (both roads after)	0·81	Yes 5%	
2	9	19	Bypasses to towns (do do)	0·67	Yes 1%	
3	18	39	Dual carriageways	0·68	Yes 5%	
4	15	37	Widening two lanes to three	0·78	Nearly (less than 10%)	
5	19	53	Realignments of two−lane roads	0·31	Highly 0·1%	
6	17	22	Roundabouts	0·42	Yes 5%	
7	7	16	Stagger crossroads	0·28	Highly 0·1%	
8	10	16	Junction improvements	0·34	Highly 0·1%	
9	7	28	Miscellaneous minor improvements	0·55	Highly 0·1%	
10	6	31	Surface dressing bends	0·13	Highly 0·1%	
	(b)	Legal	traffic engineering works			
11	5	11	Traffic signals	0·60	Yes 5%	
12	8	20	Double white lines	0·73	Indicated 10%	
13	3	5	One−way street systems	0·73	No	
14	4	31	Clearways	0·97	No	
15	3	19	Speed limits posted:−30 mile/h	0·83	No	
16	10	26	Speed limits posted:−40 mile/h	1·06	No	
17	4	11	Speed limits posted:−50 mile/h	0·75	Yes 1%	
18	10	41	Speed limits relaxed:−30 to 40	0·99	No	

TABLE 10 The observed effect on accidents of changes in road conditions

---

* J. J. Leeming, 'Road Accidents'. London': *Medicine, Science and the Law,* October 1962. Also reproduced in TEC, September 1962.

explanation. These are the mean ratios, for the sites in the sample, of the number of accidents after the change to those before. That is to say, taking line 1, Motorways, as an example, the mean number of accidents at the sites in the sample after the construction of the motorways was 0·81—or 81%—of the number which would have been expected to happen if the motorway had not been opened. The second decimal place should not be taken as reliable, and I shall approximate the figures to fractions in the text.

Columns 10 and 11 give the number of fatal accidents at the sites in the sample, respectively before and after the change. These figures are not strictly comparable, because the after periods are not always as long as the before ones. They are also subject to the usual error variations inevitable in such figures, and *should only be taken as a rough comparison.*

6	7	8	9	10	11	12	13	14
cidents after the change to those before				Total fatal accidents at all sites		Changes in accidents all sites all accidents		
Fatal and serious combined		Fatal only						
Ratio	Significance	Ratio	Significance	Before	After	+	No change	—
0·72	Yes 5%	0·93	No	98	83	—	1	4
0·88	No	0·94	No	23	26	3	4	12
0·78	No	0·75	No	47	33	7	8	24
0·90	No	0·52	Yes 5%	32	17	7	10	20
0·32	Highly 0·1%	0·25	Yes 5%	13	3	3	13	37
0·44	Yes 5%			8	2	1	4	7
0·19	Highly 0·1%			8	—	—	4	12
0·46	Very nearly 5%			9	2	—	6	10
				9	1	2	14	12
0·21	Yes 1%			7	1	—	3	28
				4	3	3	3	5
		0·78	No	15	10	—	10	10
1·05	No			4	2	1	—	3
1·02	No	0·84	No	78	54	9	9	13
				—	3	4	12	3
1·00	No	1·09	No	25	32	11	8	7
0·74	Yes 1%	1·12	No	31	22	2	2	7
0·91	No			10	13	16	14	12

Columns 12, 13, and 14 give some *rough* idea of the scatter by giving for each sample the number of sites at which there were respectively an increase, no change, or a reduction in accidents. Unless the change was at least 10%, or by not less than two accidents, it was taken that there was no change. Once again, this only gives a rough idea, and should not be taken as precise.

The figures were supplied to me in 1966 and 1962 and the after period was usually three years, so that most of the works were done in 1963 or earlier, and the civil engineering ones would be of earlier types. The table will not record the results of some of the modifications which are continually being introduced as a result of experience, so the reductions obtained may not be as large as they might be for modern works.

It is important to realize that the results given in the table are what we have achieved, not what we could achieve, partly for the reasons set out in the last paragraph, but Government policy has always been directed to the saving of money—'economy' is the jargon word—rather than to the saving of life. As a result of this, many of the civil engineering works done were substandard even at the time, so some of the figures for reductions obtained are disappointing. I have also included all the figures sent to me, even when they seemed unfavourable, and have not selected convenient ones.

3. MOTORWAYS, BYPASSES AND DUAL CARRIAGEWAYS

These are included in lines 1, 2. and 3 of Table 10. They are all somewhat similar, and are not always easy to separate. I have included the Maidstone bypass under Motorways because it is designated as one, though it might more logically be counted as a bypass.

For motorways and bypasses I have included both routes—the old one and the new one—in the after figures, so that the after figures are for roughly double the mileage of road.

As an example of this, and to illustrate the general methods of working, I take the case of the motorway M6 between Broughton and Hampson Green in Lancashire or, roughly speaking, between Preston and Lancaster, for which Mr James Drake, County Surveyor of Lancashire, very kindly did a special study for me. Figure 5 shows a small diagrammatic plan of the section and Table 11 shows the accidents. In this table column 1 gives the accidents on A6, the original road between points A and B, for two years

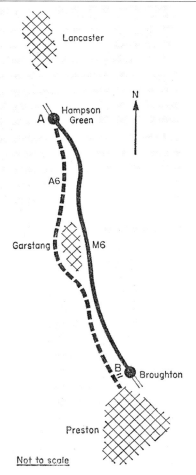

FIGURE 5 Diagrammatic plan of Motorway M6 between Hampson Green and Broughton, Lancashire

before the opening of the motorway. Column 2 gives the accidents on the same stretch of road for one year after the opening, and column 3 those on the corresponding length of motorway for the same period. These two latter figures are added together in column 4 to give the total number of accidents on the two routes combined for the year after the opening.

Column	1	2	3	4	5
Type of accident	A6 Two years before opening of motorway	One year after opening of motorway			
		A6	M6	Combined total	Expected total
Fatal	18	4	–	4	9
Serious injury	61	15	4	19	32
Slight injury	164	43	17	60	86
Total	243	62	21	83	127
Control (injury accidents in county)	20,870	10,980		Control ratio $\frac{after}{before} = 0.53$	

TABLE 11 Accidents on the A6 and the Motorway M6 in Lancashire for two years before and one year after the opening of the motorway

The bottom line of the table gives the total number of injury accidents in the whole County of Lancashire for the two years in column 1, and for the one year under columns 2 and 3. Dividing this latter number by the former one gives the control figure of 0.53. Then the numbers in column 1 are multiplied by this figure, and entered into column 5, which then gives the number of accidents which would have been expected to have taken place on A6 if the motorway had not been opened.* The motorway, then, can reasonably be thought to have reduced accidents on the two roads combined to about two-thirds of the previous number. The 70 mile/h speed limit was introduced in December 1965 and invalidates any comparison for later years.

Motorways and bypasses *generate* traffic, that is, produce extra traffic, partly by inducing people to travel who would not otherwise have done so by making the new route more convenient than the old, partly by people who go out of their direct route to

---

* This is not strictly legitimate, but it gives a rough guide to the change in accidents.

enjoy the greater convenience of the new road, and partly by people who use the towns bypassed because they are more convenient for shopping and visits when through traffic has been removed. Readers may remember the discussion in the Press recently of the fears of traffic congestion in the Lake District because the motorway M6 makes it so much easier for the traffic from industrial Lancashire to get to the Lakes.

This effect is shown by the Doncaster Bypass Motorway A1(M). A census point on A1 at Bentley, just north of the town, showed 27,400 vehicles per day in August 1959, two years before the opening of the motorway, and 29,400 v.p.d. in July 1961, the month before the opening. After the bypass was opened, 23,600 v.p.d. were recorded at Bentley on the old road, and 14,400 on the bypass itself, making 37,900 using the two routes combined, an overall increase of 30%, which is unusually large.

This increase in traffic would naturally affect the accidents, and make the effect of the motorway in reducing them less apparent at first sight. But the result of a motorway is considerable. The RRL estimated that the motorway M1 in the year after its opening made a net saving of 1,000 'casualties',* including 400 serious injuries, and 30 fatalities.

There are still some problems to be solved. The results of the works included in lines 1, 2 and 3 of Table 10 showed some inconsistency. The sample in line 1, for motorways, included the Maidstone Bypass, which was less successful than the other motorways, producing no net change in accidents. It is short for a motorway, which may account for the difference. Then the apparent effect of the dual carriageways in reducing accidents was affected by one length of the A1, which showed a substantial increase in accidents, and similarly with one of the bypasses, that at Wetherby, also on A1. Both of these cases were associated with junction trouble. At Wetherby a flyover was obviously needed for one cross roads from the start, but money was not made available at the time. It has now been constructed.

One problem not yet solved is that of vehicles out of control crossing the central reserve into the other carriageway. A rigid barrier tends to return the car back into its own carriageway even

---

* RT, p. 418ff. The figure of 11,000 given in RT is a misprint for 1,000.

more out of control, possibly with catastrophic results. A wrongly designed barrier might cause more—and more serious—accidents than no barrier at all. This problem is being studied in several countries, on the lines of flexible barriers which will hold a car. A really wide central reserve seems to be the best solution, but this is rarely practicable, as it takes too much land.

A further problem, especially on motorways, is fog. It may be worse in this country than it is in the U.S.A. There is little to guide a driver in fog conditions, and it is hard to estimate speed. I used the M4 the morning following the crashes in 1965 which got so much publicity in the Press. The fog was still thick, and I found it very noticeable that drivers were confused. Lorry rear lights were too dim for daylight conditions.

For all-purpose dual carriageways, junctions present a serious problem. When we get really safety-minded we may find that one solution would be to reduce their number by not allowing any entry to or from junctions which would involve right-hand turns, or crossing a carriageway. Special arrangements such as roundabouts or flyovers could be made for some of them at intervals. This would involve the local people wishing to enter trunk roads in some detours and inconvenience, but we must decide whether this is necessary in the interests of safety.

The table shows that the three measures included in the first three lines have reduced all accidents by a quarter, and serious ones slightly less, though motorways have reduced serious ones more than slight ones. If these seem disappointing it must be remembered that the motorways and bypasses double the mileage of road, and that the junction problem on dual carriageways has not yet been solved.

4. WIDENING TWO-LANE ROADS TO THREE-LANE ROADS

This matter is of special interest because the three-lane road is often described as a killer. This is an example of the attitude of mind which thinks that because something 'could' or 'ought' to cause accidents, argal it does. The argument is that head-on collisions occur frequently because drivers travelling in opposite directions try to pass at the same time.

Line 4 of Table 10 shows that this is not borne out by the facts. There is an overall reduction in all accidents to three-quarters of the previous, though the reduction in serious accidents is not so marked. Yet, peculiarly enough, a separate analysis on fatal accidents shows a reduction to half, which is significant at the 5% level. Thus the reduction is most marked in fatalities. The evidence, then, is that the widening to three lanes markedly reduces fatal accidents, and others to a lesser extent.

One of the sites in the sample taken in line 4 of Table 10, showed an increase in accidents after the widening, and these were associated with cars turning right out of the main road into a minor road of some local importance. This increase was large enough to affect the whole result of the sample, which otherwise would have shown a larger reduction. At a number of such junctions, including the one just mentioned, the experiment has been tried of striping the centre lane, and putting in double white lines, and this has markedly reduced the accidents at the site I have mentioned.

A dual carriageway is always better than a three-lane road, but as long as we are limited by the present policy that money is more important than lives, there is a case for the latter. Adding the third lane much reduces congestion, markedly reduces accidents, especially fatal ones, is in many cases cheaper than dual carriageways, and takes less land. A modern development which has much to be said for it is to combine a three-lane and duals, using the latter when it reduces the work necessary to get the long visibility needed for a three-lane road, or at junctions.

The cases in the sample taken in line 4 of Table 10, were all short lengths of three-lane in a predominantly congested two-lane road. Such places may be more dangerous than a long continuous stretch of three-lane road because they lead to a scramble to get past slow vehicles. This tendency is noticeable on the Bristol-Taunton Road, A38, which has occasional three-lane stretches. A long length of three-lane road may be more effective in reducing accidents. This is shown by Table 12 and Figure 6, which give the accident rates for the years from 1958 to 1965 on the same road A38 between Gloucester and Bristol, which was widened progressively to three lanes during the period covered by the table. During that time the traffic increased by about 60%, yet the total number of accidents on the whole length of the road fell in proportion to the length of three-lane road, to be finally just over 80% in 1965 of what they were in 1958, before the widening started. The accident rate per vehicle mile was thus halved.

Year	Proportion of length three–lane	Mean volume of traffic (vehicles per day)	Injury accidents	
			Total no.	No.per million v/m
1958	0	11,700	263	2·6
9	0·19	12,600	266	2·4
1960	0·23	13,400	235	2·0
1	0·41	14,500	229	1·8
2	0·49	15,800	226	1·7
3	0·52	16,100	214	1·5
4	0·82	17,400	204	1·3
5	1·00	18,800	208	1·3

TABLE 12 A38, Gloucester-Bristol. The effect on accidents, and the accident rate, of widening to three lanes

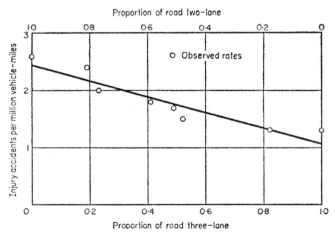

FIGURE 6 A38 Gloucester-Bristol. Change in accident rate with proportion of road widened to three lanes

54

Figure 6 shows the accident rate per vehicle mile on the road plotted against the proportion of its length which was three-lane. A straight line has been drawn on this by regression,* and the fit of this line is highly significant at less than the 0·1% level. It would thus be expected to occur by chance less than once in a thousand trials. We can think of the line as fitting the data very well indeed, and as expressing the reduction in accidents which happened on this road as it was widened from two lanes to three. These figures certainly do not support the idea that the three-lane road is a killer. The Gloucestershire figures reinforce the conclusion from line 4 of Table 10, but owing to the lack of detailed records, they could not be included in the sample for the line.

Many of the lengths of road included in the sample for line 4 were substandard according to modern ideas, so the result of widening to more up-to-date standards would be expected to be even better.

The unfavourable attitude to the three-lane road may have arisen because when fatalities do happen they are likely to be given more publicity in the Press, which may think that they are of special interest owing to the popular prejudice. It may also arise because of the concentration on the driver in the propaganda, leading people to think that if he is given an opportunity to drive dangerously he will take it, an idea which has no foundation in fact.

In some circumstances, widening to three lanes offers advantages. The Gloucester-Bristol Road may be paralleled by a motorway, but will still remain of enough local importance to justify its widening, while in the meantime its traffic capacity and accident record have been much improved by the work. It would be a pity if prejudice were to compel the Ministry to reduce the policy of widening to three lanes as long as 'economy' continues to be looked upon as more important than saving life.

---

* *Regression* is a statistical process of fitting a line to a set of figures by minimizing the sum of the squares of the differences between the observed figures and those which would be found from the line if it expressed an exact relationship.
I am indebted to Mr R. A. Downs, the County Surveyor of Gloucestershire, for these figures.

There would be less widening done, and fewer lives saved, if the three-lane road was banned.

5. THE REALIGNMENT OF TWO-LANE ROADS

This work, which the line shows is highly successful, consists of the realignment of short lengths of road of the familiar country-lane type, but which carry much less traffic than those which were widened to three lanes. It mostly consists of the elimination of bottlenecks and black spots. As the reduction was so highly significant we can be very reasonably confident that the result of such work is the reduction of all accidents—including fatal and serious ones—by about two-thirds.

6. CROSSROADS AND JUNCTIONS

A crossroads can be dealt with either by means of a flyover, a roundabout or a stagger, according to the amount of traffic on the two roads concerned. Flyovers are, no doubt, the ideal, but they are rarely possible except as part of a motorway or very large new road. I have no figures for them.

There is some prejudice against roundabouts, possibly because they may cause congestion if they are too small, or if the traffic is too great for them to cope with it. There is one on the Exeter Bypass which has acquired nation-wide notoriety, and is the scene of many serious hold-ups of traffic in summer. It is too small, and in any event a flyover is really needed at peak times, though in the winter months the roundabout is adequate enough.

Line 6 of Table 10 shows that roundabouts reduce accidents of all kinds to less than half of those before the work was done, in spite of many of them being of inadequate size, so the reduction, good though it is, is less than could be possible. What can be done is shown by Table 13, which shows the accident record at Roundhouse Cross in Dorset from 1947 to 1966. This is at the crossing of the A31 with the A350. There had been several fatal accidents there before 1939, but records were not available for these years. When four serious and fatal accidents occurred there in the two years 1947 and 1948 it was realized that the position might get very bad indeed when the traffic increased after petrol rationing was removed, so money was allotted for the roundabout out of the very small sum allowed for such work under the austerity regime of

Type of accident	Unimproved crossroads		Roundabout constructed 1949	Roundabout in operation							
	1947	1948		1950 to 1954 inc.	1955	1956	1957 & 1958	1959	1960 to 1964 inc.	1965	1966
Fatal		1									
Serious	3	–				1		1		1	
Slight					1			1			
Total	3	1		Nil	1	1	Nil	2	Nil	1	Nil

TABLE 13 Accidents at Roundhouse Cross, Dorset, from 1947 to 1966

Sir Stafford Cripps. Table 13* shows that the result was the virtual elimination of accidents. The few which did take place on the roundabout were traced to the surface's having polished. The roundabout was to full modern standards, allowing for eventual dual carriageways on both roads. Its size was much criticized locally at the time, but it was fully justified.

Where traffic is lighter, a stagger may be effective. There are two kinds, a *right-left stagger* and a *left-right stagger,* as shown in

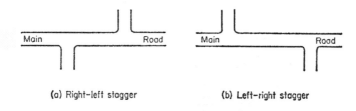

(a) Right–left stagger   (b) Left–right stagger

FIGURE 7 Diagrams of staggers

Figure 7. The terms arise from the movements a driver on the minor road has to make to cross over. In a right-left stagger he has

---

* This table has been brought up to date from one included in a paper I presented to *Symposium on Road Safety,* 1964. Dublin: Department of Local Government, Eire. There were no injury accidents there in 1967.

first to turn right into the main road, and then left out of it. In the other kind, these movements are reversed.

Right turns are the most frequent source of accidents at junctions, so right-left staggers are safer than left-right ones, and the former type is now used as far as possible, though a left-right stagger may still be much better than an unimproved crossroads.

Here, again, the table shows that staggers are highly successful, reducing all accidents to less than a third, and fatal and serious ones to less than a fifth of what they had been before, both effects being highly significant at less than the 0·1% level.

It is not always clear whether the stagger reduces accidents to crossing traffic, or works as a double-junction improvement. The full movements of vehicles are not always recorded, so we cannot be sure what route the driver intended to take. The official object of the police inquiry into accidents is only to establish whether one or other of the drivers had committed an offence, so the proposed movements of the vehicles may not be relevant to it. From the traffic engineer's angle, which is the prevention of further accidents, these movements are of vital importance. Thus, if there was no crossing traffic at all, and both side-roads acted merely as feeders to the main road, an elaborate stagger might not be needed. We may be spending a lot of money unnecessarily, merely because of the inadequacy, and wrong objective, of the accident investigation.

Junction improvements in line 8 of Table 10 comprise a number of miscellaneous works at junctions of minor roads with major ones. They include such varied work as the clearing of visibility, putting in bollards, the white line striping of the centre lane on three-lane carriageways already mentioned above (p. 53), and so on. They have been quite successful, reducing all accidents to about a third of what they had been previously and serious ones to less than half. Otherwise they do not call for any special comment.

7. MISCELLANEOUS MINOR IMPROVEMENTS

This is a very mixed batch, and includes almost any type of minor improvement which could not be taken under one or other of the former headings. They are such things as very short realignments to eliminate what were more kinks than bends, the removal of small humps, widenings of small bridges, the superelevation of bends, and so on. They seem to have halved the accidents, and the reduction is highly significant at the 0·1% level. Otherwise they call for no special comment.

8. SURFACE DRESSING BENDS

This is particularly interesting, and merits discussion in detail. I must start with a confession. When I went to Dorset in 1946, I was indoctrinated with the propaganda, and thought that skidding accidents were due to bad driving. As is so often done still, I dismissed statements by drivers that they had skidded as 'limp excuses', to use the expression of a writer of a letter to *Milestones,* the Journal of the Institute of Advanced Motorists, signing himself as 'Police Sergeant, Manchester'. My conversion took time, but it is an interesting example of G. K. Chesterton's expression 'trying to find out what will prove itself'.

There had long been complaints about some bends on a first-class road. This had a bad accident record, and was first priority on the Council's list of places for improvement. I examined them, and noticed that the surface was what we called *fat*. The tar or bitumen from the surfacing material had risen to the surface and covered the stone, which normally shows. This can get slippery when wet. I did not think this was the cause of the accidents, but had it removed by a machine, then new, called a *heater-planer*. This first heats the surface, and then planes off the surplus material. The accidents stopped, and there have been very few since.

This did not 'make the penny drop'. I took it as an isolated case. Next, complaints were made about skidding on new asphalt surfaces laid with one of the surfacing machines then being imported from the U.S.A. These skids were said by all, including the police, to be due to bad driving. But they got too frequent to be due to bad driving, and it was too much of a coincidence for them always to happen on the same material. Yet we had a lot of older examples of it in the county which gave no trouble, and it bore a very good reputation.

In the early days of my study of this matter I discussed it with a senior member of the police. He dismissed it all with the remark 'good drivers don't skid', and put it down to bad driving. Later on

59

I received a phone call from another policeman, who said I must do something about the surface at ——, one of their cars had skidded and was a write-off. I could not resist the murmur that good drivers don't skid, and it was not well received. Even the police are human; he had not heard what his colleague had said. It was the same material.

I then noticed that the new surface looked rather fatter than usual. It was hardly perceptible, but I thought it might be the source of the trouble. The new machine was fitted with a vibrating bar which rested on the surface, and partly compacted the material by its vibration before it was finished off by the roller. The bitumen used as binder is a viscous liquid when hot, and vibration brings a liquid to the surface. Neat bitumen is slippery when wetted by rain. We then reduced the bitumen content of the mixture, and had no further trouble.

This set me thinking more. It showed that the complaints were not mere limp excuses. I also found that my colleagues had had similar experiences. I therefore decided to try the experiment of surface dressing* a number of sharp bends which had bad accident records, more in hope than anything else, because there had been few complaints of skidding on them. The result was almost magical, the accidents fell to quite small numbers (cf. line 10 of Table 10, p. 46), and in some places were completely eliminated. I found that others had had similar results. My conversion was complete.

The RRL were working on the same problem, and a description of their work will be found in RS. They produced a portable tester which solved one of our problems, that of telling whether a surface is likely to be slippery. A photograph of this is shown in Plate 1. It consists of a pendulum fitted with a pad of standard size and material which can be adjusted to rub on the surface of the road for a standard distance when the pendulum is allowed to swing. The friction of the pad on the surface—which is wetted for the test—retards the swing, and reduces the extent of the return upstroke in proportion to the roughness of the surface. The extent of the retardation is recorded on the curved scale by the indicating

---

* *Surface dressing* is the spraying of hot tar or bitumen on the surface of the road, covering it with stone chippings, and rolling them in.

arm, which stays behind when the pendulum falls back. The reading on the scale gives an arbitrary figure between 0 and 1, which is called the *Skid resistance value,* and this is an indication of the slipperiness of the surface at 30 mile/h. Roughly speaking, and using round figures, an s.r.v. of 0·4 or below shows that the surface is dangerously slippery, between 0·4 and 0·6 it is doubtful, and above 0·6 it is satisfactory.

Line 10 of Table 10 shows what remarkable results have been obtained from the surface dressing of bends, the accidents being reduced to one-eighth, and serious ones to one-fifth, of what they were before the bend was dressed. This applies to all accidents, and not merely to those in bad weather, or to those in which skidding had been reported.

9. SUPERELEVATION

It is appropriate to explain here the effect of *superelevation,* which is often misunderstood. It consists in tilting the road surface downwards towards the inside of the curve. The slope produces a force tending to push a car inwards, and this counteracts some or all of the *centrifugal force* which always acts outwards on any object moving in a curved path. It will be familiar as the pull on a string if a weight is whirled round. The superelevation is, of course, built into the road, and is fixed once it is finished. It cannot counteract the centrifugal force at all speeds, so there is almost always some force acting along the road surface at right angles to the direction of travel of the car. There is, indeed, even some on a straight, because we tilt—or *camber*—the surface of the road, usually both ways from the centre, for drainage purposes. The driver, as a result of this, almost always experiences a pull on his steering, though it becomes second nature, and he does not notice it.

The force acting along the road surface is called the *lateral force.* It is usually expressed as a proportion of the weight of the vehicle. This proportion is called the *lateral ratio,* and its value is given, very nearly, by the following formula:

$$j = \frac{V^2}{15R} - a$$

In this, j is the lateral ratio, a pure number without dimensions,

V is the speed in miles per hour, R is the radius of the curve in feet and *a* is the superelevation, expressed as a slope. Figure 8 is a graph of the lateral ratio plotted against speed for some typical superelevated curve. At slow speeds, below that shown as V_h, the lateral force is negative. It will act inwards towards the centre of the curve, and a vehicle would slide inwards if the surface was frictionless. At the speed V_h there will be no lateral force, and a car with well-designed steering, and properly inflated tyres, would steer itself round the curve, without the driver needing to steer it. For this reason, that speed is called the *hands-off speed*. The value of V_h expressed in mile/h will vary with the radius of the curve and its superelevation.

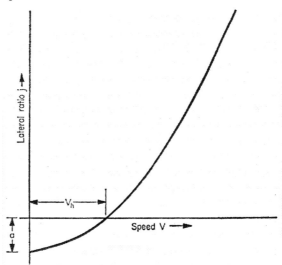

FIGURE 8 Graph of lateral ratio on a superelevated curve

It follows from this that, unless a minimum speed limit could be fixed and strictly enforced, we must not provide too much superelevation, or slow vehicles will tend to slide down into the path of the faster ones. This happened on the old Brooklands racing track, which was very highly banked. A driver misjudged his speed, took the banking too high, slid down into the path of a faster car, and one of the drivers was killed. This could happen on an ordinary road under icy conditions.

At speeds much above the hands-off, the lateral force acting on a car on a bend will go up very nearly in proportion to the square of the speed, so that a 40% rise in speed would double the force. On a very sharp bend, this could happen at quite slow speeds.

This is all somewhat of a simplification. A vehicle's stability on a curve is also affected by its design. This will be explained further by Mackay (10.2, p. 118).

10. SOME CONCLUSIONS

Table 10 (p. 46) has shown that road improvements do reduce accidents, often very dramatically. They usually do this by removing some trap or other set by the road conditions. In later sections, I shall discuss some of these traps, but first of all we may consider the surface dressing of bends because this has much to teach us.

The dramatic reduction in accidents, to an eighth of what they were before the dressing of the surface, shows clearly that drivers could estimate the curvature of the bends well enough to avoid accident, and that they did so. Provided the surface is non-skid, and the car is in good condition and well designed, a sharp curve does not present any real danger, but if a driver slightly miscalculates his speed—and I have shown in the last section that the lateral force goes up approximately as the square of the speed—a skid may result if the surface has polished, especially if the car has much over-steer (10.2, p. 118). This may be more likely to happen in wet weather, because surfaces are more slippery when wet. This is usually called 'bad driving', but it seems remarkable that this bad driving almost always occurs when the surface has polished, which may be when it still looks rough. It is a superficial view to dismiss it as bad driving like this. The surface must have played some part.

When the accidents occurred in the fog in 1965—the occasion which made the excuse for the 70 mile/h speed limit—they were imputed by everyone to bad driving, and a chorus of abuse of drivers appeared in the Press. Yet at about the same time a report by members of the staff of the RRL on accidents on the M1 was published in the technical press. In this was a table which told engineers that the road's surface was highly slippery—a conclusion which was not surprising to some. It never occurred to anyone but these engineers to ask what part the surface had played in the accidents. The official attitude was just to slap on a speed limit and all would then be well.

In a great many cases skidding is not reported to the police. At one very sharp bend on the Shaftesbury-Sherborne Road, A30, in Dorset, there were sixteen accidents in three years before the bend was dressed, and none at all in the next year after it. The surface polished again and there were one or two more before another dressing was repeated. *Skidding was only reported in four of these.* Yet the fact that the dressing practically eliminated the accidents shows that there must have been skidding in most, if not all, of the sixteen. Absence of reports of skidding should not be taken as an indication that all is well with the surface. If such reports are made, however, they should be looked into at once.

In my later years in Dorset, I had a routine standing order to my traffic department to test the surface of the road with the RRL tester if any sudden increase of accidents showed up on the accident maps. It was almost always found that the surface had polished and a dressing put the matter right. We also found that some stones thought to have good non-skid properties were liable to polish after a time, though they continued to look rough. One stone which had a very good reputation even had to be banned completely. It was good for a time, and then polished suddenly and unpredictably.

It is only fair to add that these results do not wholly agree with those found by the RRL. They did not find such an outstanding reduction in all accidents, as opposed to those on wet surfaces. Nevertheless, my results are based on a large sample from six widely spread counties, and are, I feel, fully reliable. My conclusions are based on long practical experience.

11. AN EXAMPLE OF A TRAP

I will now return to Warmwell Cross, which I used above (5.2, p. 39) as an example of the factors present in accidents. Figure 9 is a diagrammatic plan of the site. It is not to scale. The place looked like a square crossroads of the usual type. But it was not really quite typical. The real main road is that from Weymouth to Wareham,

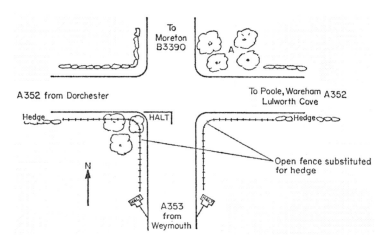

FIGURE 9 Diagrammatic plan of Warmwell Cross, Dorset

that is, from the south round to the east. This also leads to Poole, Bournemouth, Lulworth Cove and the Purbeck Hills, all much frequented by tourists. The road to the west goes to Dorchester, and that to the north is a second-class road of local importance. These two roads carry much less traffic than the real main road. The layout is really an important main road making a very sharp right angle bend, with two minor roads joining there to form a crossroads.

All the accidents happened to cars coming from the south, and they collided with vehicles, mostly lorries, coming from the east and going in the Dorchester direction, that is, from east to west. At first they were relatively minor, but they were a source of worry, and we began to study them. It soon appeared that cars coming from the south were disobeying the Halt sign on a large scale, and that many of them did not seem to be trying to stop. Other junctions in the district with Halt signs were watched, and conduct similar to that at Warmwell Cross was so rare that it could be said to be unique.

The observers also noticed that some of the drivers who disobeyed the sign showed evident signs of confusion, and some who had shot across into the northern road were seen to return a little later, looking confused and showing signs of having lost their

65

way. One or two even asked their way when they got back to the crossroads.

At first, the Halt sign had been of the early, small, type, and as soon as the large one became available, one was put up, as it was thought that the old one was hard to see. This had no effect. Then a second large one was put on the right-hand side of the road, again without effect, though both could be seen from a long way away.

In the meantime, many motorists had been prosecuted. In five years there were a hundred convictions for offences ranging from failing to obey the Halt sign to 'killing by dangerous driving'.

Of course, all sorts of suggestions were made by the local people, and all that were practicable were tried without any apparent effect. After one of the fatalities, the hedges were removed on the two corners on the Weymouth side, and replaced by open fences. The trees in the small groves on the corners, shown on the plan, were fine beeches with little undergrowth, did not block the view, and were not on the corners involved in the accidents. Everyone locally said that the problem was solved and that there would be no more accidents, but there were, and they even seemed to be worse.

Some time during our studies, we tried the experiment of posting a policeman, with a wireless set, in the trees at point A on Figure 9. On the three roads to the north, east and west were posted other policemen, similarly equipped, each with a member of my department beyond him. When the man at A phoned that a driver had passed the sign, the policeman down the road stopped him, and merely said that we were studying an accident black spot, asking him to speak to the member of my staff, who made no reference to the sign, but asked for the driver's help—which in all cases appeared to be willingly given—and asked him what he had noticed about the place.

On the first day that this was going on, the local correspondent of the late *Sunday Dispatch* got to hear about it and came to see the Chief Constable and myself. He said that motorists were escaping punishment. He also saw some County Councillors, and a report appeared in the paper the following Sunday (*Sunday Dispatch*, 19.2.61), so the experiment was dropped, after one day.

But one of the drivers interviewed gave us the vital clue. Figure 10 shows a diagrammatic section through the approach road from Weymouth. The driver was coming along a straight road rising towards the crossroads, and he could see the Halt signs and the groves of trees. The latter looked continuous, and the gap through which the Dorchester Road ran could not be seen easily. The Halt signs only told him that he had to halt somewhere between there and John o'Groats! *They did not tell him where to halt.* The actual spot where he was to stop was indicated by a continuous white line, and the word Halt painted on the road.

It is often claimed that words or lines painted on the road are better than signs at the side of the road. So they are, *if the road is concave upwards.* If it is flat, they are foreshortened and are less easy to see, but *when the road is convex upwards, they may be hidden completely until the driver is almost on them.* This is what happened here. The words and lines on the road were hidden by a

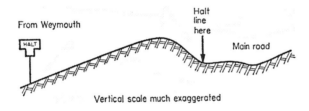

FIGURE 10
Diagrammatic section of Warmwell Cross, Dorset

short sharp brow, and were invisible until the driver got to within about fifty feet or so of them, too late to stop safely. See Table 9 (p. 32) for safe stopping distances.

To add to the deception, when the driver was coming down the straight from Weymouth, he could not see the Wareham-Dorchester Road. It was hidden from him by a combination of slight swells in the intervening ground, and by its being in a very small cutting, almost imperceptible, but just enough to hide the road. The general appearance of the place, with the apparently continuous grove of trees, made it look as if the so-called major road was displaced northward by a short distance.

67

Probably, therefore, drivers approached the crossroads fully intending to stop and obey the law, but thinking they had to do so further on. When they saw the Halt line it was too late to stop. A simple trap, but a lethal one.

It will reasonably be asked why did we not see this for ourselves? The answer is that we knew the place so well that it did not occur to us. We knew where the Halt line was, and where to stop, without needing signs to tell us. Moreover, do not forget the all-pervading propaganda. Even engineers cannot help being affected by it. We are told that accidents are caused 'nearly always by simple human error', as the Minister's Foreword to the 1959 Highway Code tells us. Fair enough, but he forgot to tell us that the human error may have a cause.

Now there is a roundabout at Warmwell Cross, which fortunately was in the pipeline at the time of the experiment. It was needed on traffic grounds, as the Halt sign caused severe congestion in summer. Table 14 shows the result of this roundabout; it eliminated fatal accidents for five years after its construction. There were no injury accidents there in 1967.

Type of accident	Unimproved crossroads														Roundabout Under cons		Open			
	1947	1948	1949	1950	1951	1952	1953	1954	1955	1956	1957	1958	1959	1960	1961	1962	1963	1964	1965	1966
Fatal	—	—	—	—	—	—	—	—	—	—	1	—	—	2			—	—	—	—
Serious	—	—	—	—	1	2	—	—	—	2	3	—	1	—			—	1	1	—
Slight	1	1	1	1	—	2	—	—	—	3	1	—	1	—			—	—	—	—
Total	1	1	1	1	1	4	—	—	—	5	5	—	2	2			—	1	1	—

TABLE 14 Accidents at Warmwell Cross, Dorset, from 1947 to 1966

The list of factors in the fatal accident taken above (5.2, p. 40) will now be discussed, the letters referring to the letters in that section. (*a*) Chance entered into it because the car and lorry happened to arrive at the same spot simultaneously (5.4, p. 41). Many other cars had crossed the Halt line without collision. (*b*) The driver certainly made a mistake. (*c*) This mistake was due to the deception in the layout. If this had not been present, or if the roundabout had been there, he would not have made the mistake. (*d*i) If, instead of prosecuting drivers, the inquiry was devoted to stopping accidents the trap would have been found out much earlier, and remedied. (*d*ii) The Halt sign's being some unknown distance from the place where the driver had to stop, and the line's being hidden by the brow, contributed to the trap. If the sign had been at the Halt line, like the continental one, and our new one, the trap might not have been there. (*d*iii) The main-road drivers being mostly local, or knowing the road well, knew the Halt signs were there, and were encouraged to drive straight over. In one of the prosecutions, the main-road driver admitted as much in his evidence, and said he could not see the car on the Weymouth Road. Learned Judge said he had done no wrong. But from intimate knowledge of the place, I know that he *could*, and should, have seen the car, but it was like the 'Invisible Man' in the story of that title in the *Innocence of Father Brown* by G. K. Chesterton. In this story, several witnesses swore that no one had entered a block of flats in which a murder had been committed. But the postman actually had done so, and he had done the murder, and carried out the body in his sack. He was *mentally invisible* as Father Brown put it. In the same way, the car was mentally invisible to the driver on the main road. His subconscious mind no doubt saw it but, as he felt certain it would halt, his conscious mind did not register it, and he was not prepared for it to drive out. (*e*) We are left to speculate about the part that drink played.

12. LESSONS TO BE LEARNT

There is not the space for me to give more examples, but one clear conclusion can be drawn from these studies, that by no means all accidents are due to wilful and deliberate bad driving. They may be due to error of judgement, ignorance, incompetence, carelessness, but these are all human characteristics, and are not confined to drivers. They cause many other accidents as well as road ones. The results of these errors seem to happen very often to people who are honestly trying to do their best—such as it is—and trying to avoid an accident. Their best may not be very good, but it is their best.

Here again the slippery surfaces are specially instructive. In many cases, the surfaces looked perfectly rough and non-skid, and, indeed, we engineers thought them so until we learnt better as a result of experience, and by disregarding the propaganda. But if *we* thought them so, how can we reasonably expect an ordinary motorist to know better than we do?

There is, therefore, compelling reason to think that some proportion, perhaps a large one, of the accidents is due to some trap or deception in road conditions, either in the layout; or in the design of signs, and furthermore, that those traps cannot be found out because the law prevents the engineers from doing so.

It is quite impossible, even for an experienced engineer, to say whether a place will have accidents. The ordinary man certainly cannot do this. I frequently got letters from local Councils, Road Safety Committees or private individuals couched in these words: 'May we draw your attention to the highly dangerous spot at ———? Something must be done before someone is killed!' But unless this place had been already known for its accident record—when it would have shown up on my accident maps, and have been down on the Council's list for improvement—it was never really necessary for me to ask if there had been any accidents there. There never had been!

A typical case occurred to me in my early days as a County Surveyor. There had been a minor accident, and the Parish Council wrote to me ordering the instant—and costly—improvement of a narrow bend in a cutting on a very minor road 'before someone was killed', and asked me to meet them on the site to discuss it. I explained to them that nothing could be done because the Government had banned all such improvements. I had very hard work to convince them that the County Council could not disobey the Government.

Before we parted, I 'innocently' asked them about a junction a short distance down the road, and was assured unanimously and emphatically, that it was quite all right, perfect visibility, no accidents, nothing needed doing there! *Yet nothing has been done to the 'dangerous' place, and it has still to have a second accident, while* the 'safe' place developed into an accident black spot, and indeed had already had several accidents at the time when the locals said it was safe. I knew that, but they did not.

Some years later, I put before my Committee an accident black spot map, to help them to decide on a programme for improvements, and a Councillor from the same district said that my map was nonsense. He brushed aside my explanation that it was based on accident records, and said that the local people could tell me much better where the black spots were. He gave me a list of these places, and I had the accidents looked up. *Not one of these 'black spots' had had a single accident, and they all continued to be accident-free for a number of years.* One cannot tell an accident black spot just by inspection or local knowledge. It is essential to have accident maps.

It can safely be said that places which look dangerous do not have accidents, or very few. They happen at places which do not look dangerous. The reason for this is simple. The motorist is as intelligent as the 'local people'. If a place looks dangerous, he can see that it is so, he takes care and there are no accidents. He does not want to have an accident, and he will take care at obviously dangerous places. Accidents happen when there is some trap in road conditions which is not obvious at a glance, or where the conditions are too complicated for the limited human machine to deal with in the short time available. The driver has only a fraction of a second to size up a situation, and there may be some trap which he cannot see in this short time.

These traps can often be removed quite easily. I was once ordered to put up a whole battery of signs at a bend where there had been some non-injury accidents, which had involved heavy damage. I replied that signs were clearly not the answer because traffic had been using the place for years—it was on an important road—without accident, and these had started suddenly. Needless to say, I was abused, but on inspection I found that on an exceptionally hot day the bitumen from an old dressing had come to the surface and was slippery. Heating and planing put the matter right, and there were no more accidents.

Some of his friends once told my Divisional Surveyor that at a bend which they had used for years, they had recently found themselves shooting off the road into the field. No damage was done, but it was naturally rather disconcerting. It was then found that the superelevation of the curve was wrongly designed, by having been put on too late, so that the beginning of the curve was un-superelevated. A five-ton load of surfacing material put the matter right. The locals knew the curve, and knew how to allow for the wrong design, but the approach had been surfaced with one of the new machines I have already mentioned. These made the road so much smoother running that people started to drive slightly faster quite unconsciously, just fast enough to be affected by the wrong design.

The improvements work, then, by removing some trap or other or by presenting a less complicated problem to the unreliable and inaccurate machine, the human being. While the table shows that improvements both can, and do, very materially reduce accidents, I would be the last to claim that they can stop all accidents, and, in spite of what Ministers and others have said, as quoted at the top of the chapter, I have never met anyone who has made this claim. Nevertheless, it is highly probable that a very large reduction in accidents could be made by properly designed improvements carried out for that end, and not cut down to save money, as has been the practice in the past.

13. INCREASING ACCIDENTS

There is one type of 'improvement' which does probably increase accidents. It is not included in Table 10, because no recent figures are available. Shortly after the war it was found that resurfacing the road without improving the alignment seemed to increase accidents, as in the curve mentioned above. The RRL studied this, and found that the mean *increase* in accidents, produced by this type of work, was 20% if some minor reconstruction of the alignment was done, and 65% if the surface was improved without doing any other work.

This type of work which produces a 65% increase in accidents, *is just that type of work which has been forced on us by successive governments since the war.* Sir Stafford Cripps started it, but the others have continued it, and it is still being done. We engineers have been protesting in the strongest terms, to no purpose. We have been compelled to do work—and waste money—on work we know will increase accidents. Successive governments have paid no attention to the RRL's conclusions.

The cause of this may be the speeding-up effect already mentioned opposite. It may not have so much effect now that drivers are accustomed to the machine-laid surfaces, which are universal, but we are not sure of this.

7

LEGAL ENGINEERING AND SPEED LIMITS

Life-saving Limit
'No speed limit—anywhere, any time, any place—has ever increased the number of accidents.'
Adam Raphael in 'About Motoring'. The Guardian, *26.6.1966*

'The evidence is fairly conclusive that speed limits, both in Britain and elsewhere, markedly reduce speeds and casualties, even though they are not universally obeyed.'
Rt Hon. Mrs Barbara Castle, M.P., Minister of Transport.
Quoted in The Times, *6.5.66*

I. LEGAL ENGINEERING GENERALLY

I have used the term *Legal engineering* to mean traffic engineering measures which depend for their effect on some regulation or law, in contrast to the civil engineering works described in the last chapter, which directs traffic by some physical alteration in the road layout.

Legal engineering measures depend for any success that they may have on the regulation or law being founded on some principle that is of real value for safety. This may seem to be what Mr Punch calls a 'glimpse of the obvious', but it is usually forgotten, and most of our legal measures are really based on hunch, or on the idea that anything which penalizes or restricts motorists is *ipso facto* good.

It is not always possible to find out the effect of legal measures by before-and-after studies, but those which it has been possible to study are included in the lower part of Table 10 (p. 46).

2. TRAFFIC LIGHTS

The sites in the sample were all in the fringe areas of towns or in rural areas. In towns it is harder to sort out the changes, and variations in pedestrian flow may complicate the problem. These need more intensive study than I have been able to do. In the fringe areas the problem is simpler, and the line in Table 10 may be taken as fairly representative of them. The lights have reduced accidents by about one-third, and the change is significant at the 5% level.

This reduction may be smaller than would be possible because the lights are sometimes hard to see when the sun is shining, and at night they are often mixed up with other lights. As Pole has mentioned (11.2, p. 132) the lenses are made different shapes in Switzerland, and there is much to be said for this. They could also with great advantage be made brighter by day and dimmed at night. It should not be hard to arrange this by means of some photo-electric cell device. The regulation against other lights near traffic lights should be more strictly enforced.

3. DOUBLE WHITE LINES

These lines were mostly on rural two-lane roads of the country-lane type usual in England, though some were on roads of more modern type.

Line 12 of Table 10 shows a possible decrease in accidents of about a quarter as a result of the laying of the lines, though this is only indicated at the 10% level, and we cannot be fully confident that the result is real. An extensive study in Gloucestershire shortly after the lines were put down, showed no change at all.

Type of line	Ratio $\frac{after}{before}$	
	Slight and non–injury accidents	Fatal and serious accidents
Lane lines (i.e. normal short dashes)	0·95	0·98
Hazard lines (long dashes)	0·92	0·90
Prohibitory sections (solid line one or both sides)	0·84	0·82
Whole road, all accidents	0·86	

TABLE 15 Double white lines.
Before-and-after analysis by type of line, Dorset

Table 15 shows a more detailed study I was able to make of the effect of the lines on the A31 in Dorset, a length of just over fifty miles which was divided into stretches for the study, according to the type of line laid, and the date of laying it, and the results were combined by Tanner's method. The diagram, Figure 11, explains the terms used. The lane lines are the short dashes where visibility is good, the hazard lines are the long dashes used where visibility is less good and more care is needed, and the prohibitory lines are those with a solid line on one

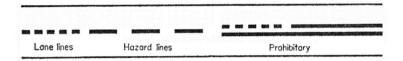

| Lane lines | Hazard lines | Prohibitory |

FIGURE 11 Types of double white lines

or both sides. The sample was not large enough to enable the effect of complete prohibition of overtaking—that is with solid lines on both sides—to be separated out. The table shows a slight reduction in accidents throughout, but none of these figures is significant, so we must doubt whether the changes are real.

These samples are fairly large, and cover between two and three hundred miles of road between them, so we cannot feel any real confidence that the lines have materially reduced accidents. The most we can say is that we can suspect that they have made a slight reduction, but we are not entitled to say that they have certainly done so.

It is possible that part of their lack of real success is that they are mandatory, and crossing them is an absolute offence. They might be more effective if they were made advisory, like some of the speed limits in the U.S.A., so that a motorist is not absolutely prohibited from crossing them, but if he got into trouble when on the wrong side of them he would have to clear himself. At present, with the absolute prohibition, they can cause intense congestion, with long queues of traffic behind agricultural tractors, or even pedal cycles. In many of these cases, one or two cars just following the obstacle could nip past and help to ease the congestion. The often unnecessary crawl may cause frustration, help to lead to driver fatigue on long journeys, and may very likely cause accidents.

The offset double white line experiment on three-lane roads has been dropped, so we need not consider it. As line 4 of Table 10 shows, the danger it is intended to guard against is largely imaginary. Here, again, the reason for the lack of success may be its being mandatory instead of advisory. It often causes intense, and totally unnecessary, congestion and frustration.

4. ONE-WAY STREETS

According to the sample in line 13 of Table 10, one-way streets reduce accidents generally, but make no change in serious and fatal accidents. The sample of the latter is small, and may have been affected by a relative failure in one town in the sample. One or two other towns taken individually, notably Torquay, gave significant reductions in accidents, without relative change in severity, the serious and fatal accidents being reduced in the same proportion as others. In Torquay it had been feared that the one-way system might increase accidents in the areas of the town not affected by the one-way system, but this has not proved to be the case. The accidents in those areas did not show any significant change, either in number or severity.

A really good one-way system can probably be relied upon to reduce accidents, but if instituted in unsuitable places it may not do so. Pedestrians may have less difficulty in crossing the street when traffic is only travelling in one direction, and some contribution may also be made by making the traffic more random, and so giving larger gaps for pedestrians to cross. I have, however, no evidence of this.

This, of course, is only discussing accidents. The very marked effect of one-way streets in reducing congestion is not relevant to this book.

5. CLEARWAYS

A *clearway* is a length of road on which it is forbidden to stop on the carriageway except in emergency. This is always thought to be a most valuable safety measure, but the evidence from the table is that it is not successful, there being no change either in 'all accidents', or in 'serious and fatal' ones. There does seem to be a slight reduction in fatal accidents, but this is not significant. The apparently large reduction in fatals shown in line 14 column 11 of Table 10 is because some of the lengths which had the largest number of them only had an after-period of one year, so the number of fatals in the after-period would be expected to be about a third of those in the before one.

I am surprised at this result, but as the sample is a fairly large

77

one, covering about one hundred miles of clearway, we can have some confidence in it. There is something to be said for them on traffic grounds, but that is not relevant here. One essential is that plenty of lay-bys should be provided to enable people to stop if they need to do so, and of course this applies specially to buses. One does see them stopping on clearways—and, incidentally, on double white lines—without drawing into a lay-by. Buses should not be exempt from the law like this.

6. SPEED LIMITS: THE EVIDENCE

The public has complete faith in speed limits as a panacea for all accidents, and the statements made by Adam Raphael and Mrs Castle, quoted at the head of this chapter, are quite typical. Goen in the U.S.A. has claimed that the accidents could be reduced to almost any amount by speed limits, the extent of the reduction being only limited by what people are prepared to stand in the cost of the reduction in speed, while in this country, the Pedestrians Association has advocated an overall speed limit of 50 mile/h, which it was claimed would cut accidents by 50%.

In spite of what Mrs Castle said, the evidence in favour of speed limits is both ambiguous and contradictory, *provided one considers all the evidence.* Much of the case in favour of them is based on the habit of sweeping inconvenient evidence under the carpet. Adam Raphael's statement is wildly at variance with the facts. Columns 12, 13 and 14 on lines 15, 16 and 17 of Table 10 (p. 47) show that out of 56 lengths of road on which speed limits were posted, less than a third, namely 17, reduced accidents, in 22 cases there was no appreciable change, and another 17 lengths were followed by an *increase* in accidents. The 40 and 50 mile/h limits also show an *increase* in fatal accidents, of 9% and 12% respectively Neither of these is statistically significant, but they support each other, so we must suspect that the increase might be real until more evidence is produced.

The sample for the 30 limit is derived mainly from the 1962 study. Few of this type of limit have been posted recently, the modern tendency being to impose 40s rather than 30s, or to relax some of the more anomalous 30s to 40. The sample shows a reduction of about 1/12th in accidents, though this is not significant. It was not possible to analyse the more serious accidents, but the only two modern limits which included fatal ones, both showed an *increase in the fatals.*

It is always claimed as 'proof' of the value of the 30 limit, that the deaths fell by over 800 in 1935, the first year it was posted, compared with 1934, the last year without a limit. This direct comparison is not valid for several reasons. 1934 was a peak year both for 'no motor vehicle deaths' and for motor vehicle ones. If 1935 is compared with the mean of the three previous years, the fall in deaths is just over 600.

The argument that the whole of the fall in deaths is attributable to the speed limit is quite untenable. Other measures, including pedestrian crossings, were taken that year, and it is quite impossible to think that they did not save some lives. Then 1935 was also virtually the end of the 'economy' campaign, so it is possible that an unusually large number of road improvements were completed that year, and this must have made some contribution to the reduction in deaths.

A before-and-after study of the 1935 limit was made in Oxfordshire, by Bennett. He compared the accidents on all the stretches of road in the county made subject to the limit for two years before, and two years after, the posting of the limit. The result is given in Table 16. This shows that there was no real change in the accidents in the built-up areas of the county as a result of the limit. The fall in fatalities is quite consistent with random variations, and is partly accounted for by the opening of the Oxford Northern bypass in May 1935, which diverted traffic from a very notorious black spot, at which there had been several fatalities, and this place was improved later in the year, as it was still thought to be dangerous for local traffic. Since the bypass was opened there have not been any fatal accidents there. It was in the built-up area, so this improvement might very likely account for *at least* one of the reductions in fatalities in 1935. The bypass might also have saved one or two others, because it avoided some lengths of road with bad accident records, as well as the City of Oxford itself. This shakes the evidence of the 1935 reduction in deaths as an effect of the speed limit. Bennett's before-and-after was the only direct evidence we have, and has been ignored. The rest is an inference from general figures. These are always unreliable.

Line 16 of Table 10 shows that 40 mile/h limits posted on roads

Type of accident	Number of accidents	
	Two years before	Two years after
Fatal	11	8
Injury	280	296
Non-injury	371	337
Total	662	641

TABLE 16 Oxfordshire. Accidents in 'built-up' areas of the county before and after the posting of the 30 mile/h speed limit in 1935.

not before subject to a limit have, if anything, slightly increased accidents, and the largest increase was in fatal accidents, though neither of these was significant. But out of the sample of 22 posted limits, five showed a *substantial increase* in fatals, of at least one before to three after. One of these was from three before to nine after, which is a very serious rise. Only once did the limit show a decrease of the same type, from six before to two after. It will also be seen from columns 12, 13 and 14 of the table, that half of the 40 limits produced a marked rise in accidents. As the sample is a fairly large one, this shows that the 40 limit is not successful.

Line 17 of the table shows that the 50 mile/h limit may be more successful, but the sample is a smaller one, and most of the sites were in Cambridgeshire, on flatter and straighter roads than prevail in the rest of the country, so its evidence is less representative, and should not be accepted as showing that a fall of about a third in accidents would result if an overall limit of 50 mile/h was imposed in the whole country, even though the fall is significant. In any event, *there was again a rise in fatals,* though this is not significant, but taken with the rise after the 40 limit, and the rise in the only two 30 limits with fatalities, we may suspect that it might be real.

The only information available on the 70 limit is in RRL Special Report No. 5 which has recently been given publicity in the Press.

The reduction found on the all-purpose roads was very small, and is suspect. The report shows that about 64 miles of motorway were opened in 1966, and, on the analogy of M1, this length of motorway would be expected to have saved between twenty and thirty deaths that year, and a corresponding number of injury accidents. It is also almost certain that a large number of road improvements were finished that year. It does not appear from the Report that any detailed study was made of the effect of the improvements, though they must have had some effect, and we must suspend judgement of the effect of the limit. It is not impossible that it might have increased accidents.

On the motorways a reduction of about 20% in injury accidents is claimed. In view of the doubtful effect of other limits, however, it might again be wiser to await more evidence, especially on fatal accidents.

The results given in Table 10 for speed limits do not materially differ from those obtained by the RRL. Their changes for the limits, apart from the 70 mile/h on the motorways, are not significant, and they are based on smaller samples than mine. I feel, then, that the best opinion that can be expressed as to the value of speed limits is 'not proven'. The RRL, however, have not analysed fatal accidents. As far as the evidence goes, and all my samples except that for the 50 limit are reasonably large, they indicate no change except for the possibility that the 40 and 50 limits may increase fatal accidents. This is also strengthened by the conclusion from a large sample that relaxing 30 limits to 40 also makes no change in accidents. Certainly, the evidence I have been able to get lends no support of any sort, and even refutes the ideas of Goen and the Pedestrians Association that lower speed limits would make a dramatic reduction in deaths. It is more probable that they might have the reverse effect, and increase them.

The statement made by Mrs Castle that there is conclusive evidence that speed limits materially reduce accidents, cannot be accepted. There is no such conclusive evidence.

7. THE PUBLIC ATTITUDE TO SPEED LIMITS

In the RRL special report on the 70 mile/h speed limit, a study was made of the attitude of motorists towards the limit, and it was found that a majority were in favour. I fail to see the point of this study. It was a foregone conclusion, because everyone, strangely enough including motorists themselves, is in favour of restrictions on motorists, and everyone indoctrinated with the propaganda which says that punishment and repression of motorists is the solution of the problem. Neither can I see the relevance of the study, because what we want to know is whether the limit stops accidents. Whether people like it or not is not material to that. I am surprised that the majority in favour was so small.

The public has a complete and touching faith in the limits. At a sherry party, given by the lady members of the County Council to the wives of the Chief Officers, a lady member went up to my wife and said: 'Your husband is *murdering* our children!'

I had opposed an application for a speed limit on a straight wide road, entirely free from any buildings but a new school. There was a good footpath, divided from the road by a green verge. I argued at Committee (*a*) that a speed limit would *not* protect the children; (*b*) that the danger, if any, was there for only an hour or two in the day, and then only for about two hundred days in the year; (*c*) that out of school hours the motorist could do any speed he liked without danger; and (*d*) that, if there was a danger, the responsibility rested with those who had put what they themselves admitted to be a danger in that place. Also, that to punish a motorist because what he was doing might be a danger in an hour's, or a week's, or a month's time—according to circumstances—but not at the time it was done, was a monstrous tyranny. The Committee accepted my argument, and the limit was not posted. That was ten years or so ago, and there still has not been an accident.

It has many times been said to me when I have asked why a limit has been wanted, and what was the danger: 'Oh, well, we know it won't stop accidents, but it will enable the police to prosecute motorists!'

On one length of road there was a strong local agitation for a speed limit. Analysis of the accidents showed that there were none associated with high speeds, but there were some associated with vehicles stopping at a shop, so the Council provided a lay-by there, which seemed to stop these accidents. At about the same time the Parish Council took the law into its own hands, as could be done in those days, by putting up some rudimentary street lighting, so that the limit had to be posted, although it was opposed by everyone, including the police. In the three years before the posting of the limit, there had been twelve accidents. In the three years after, there were nineteen, in spite of the lay-by having reduced the accidents at the shop, so it is probable that the limit produced a substantial increase in accidents. As was my usual practice, I reported this to the local Road Safety Committee. At the meeting the Parish Council representative said: *'My Council doesn't mind if the accidents have increased. We have got our speed limit!'* The Road Safety Committee supported him!

After some years of agitation on the part of the public, supported by the police, the limit was raised to 40 mile/h. *There was no change in the rate of accidents.* The mental obliquity of people who impose a limit to make the road safer, and then do not mind when the accidents increase, is almost unbelievable. But it happened!

At one place there was a strong agitation for a speed limit because there had been a fatal accident. There had been one—*an old man in the eighties knocked down by a small boy on a pedal cycle.*

I could multiply such cases.

8. EVIDENCE FROM THE U.S.A.

The evidence from the U.S.A. is as ambiguous and contradictory as that from this country. In the analysis by Allgaier and Yaksich, it was found that whether states had speed limits or not made no difference to whether their death rate was above or below prediction by the formula. This is not strong evidence, but it is some indication that speed limits do not have a very marked effect on accidents.

It seems that on the Pennsylvania Turnpike, the accident rate was the highest during the wartime 35 mile/h speed limit, imposed to save fuel and tyres. The evidence from the Parkways in the New York area is as contradictory. Some with low and strictly enforced limits have more accidents than those with higher limits less strictly enforced.*

Professor A. L. Goodhart, former President of the Pedestrians Association, claims as 'proof' of the value of speed limits, that the

---

* Robert L. Schwartz, 'The Case for Fast Drivers'. *Harper's Magazine,* September 1963.

death rate in the state of Connecticut, fell after Governor—now Senator—Ribicoff started in 1956 a campaign to enforce the speed limits in the state by suspending the licences of drivers caught 'speeding'.*

Figure 12 shows the death rates in the state annually from 1946

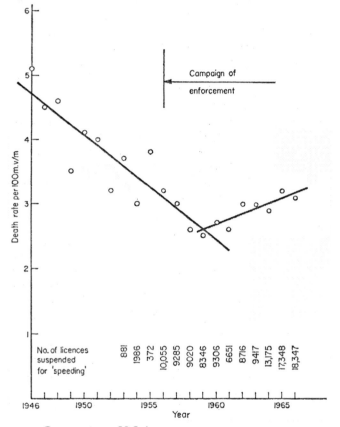

FIGURE 12 Connecticut, U.S.A.
Death rate in the state from 1946–66

---

* I put the word 'speeding' in inverted commas because it is a pejorative word, tending—and probably intended—to introduce prejudice.

to 1966. On to these I have added two regression lines, which are both significant at the 1% level,* and also at the bottom the number of licences suspended in the state for 'speeding'. From this it will be seen that while the rate in 1956 was lower than that for 1955, it was actually higher than that for 1954, and the same as that for 1952, while all the rates are part of a trend which had been going on steadily since 1946. The difference between the points and the trend line—including those after the enforcement campaign—is quite consistent with the usual fluctuations in such figures. But it will also be seen that the trend abruptly changed to one of increase round about 1959 and that, while the suspensions of licences are steadily increasing, so is the accident rate.

This sudden rise in the trend of the death rate is also shown by the states of Massachusetts and New Jersey, though in Maine and Rhode Island it is not marked. The figures for the two latter states show more fluctuations, and might not be inconsistent with a general downward trend.

Goodhart also claims as 'proof' of the success of Ribicoff's campaign, that Connecticut's rate is the lowest in the Union. It is not, Rhode Island's is. In any case, Allgaier and Yaksich predicted that Connecticut and Rhode Island would be among the states with the lowest rate.

These figures certainly show no confirmation of Goodhart's claim that the enforcement campaign was a success, and are much more likely to be evidence that it was a failure. It has, indeed, been condemned by Nader, whose book *Unsafe at any Speed,* was given wide publicity lately, and by the very distinguished traffic engineer Professor Daniel P. Moynihan. The rise in the rate about 1959 may be due to some tendency in the U.S.A. as a whole, as it is shown by other states.

In Nebraska it was found that the relaxation of speed limits was sometimes followed by a marked decrease in accidents, especially fatal ones, and the official instructions for posting

---

* The figures from which this diagram is plotted are from *Facts 1959* and *Facts 1966,* published annually by the State Motor Vehicle Department. I have added the regression lines. In the U.S.A. annual publications *Accident Facts19* .. the figures do not agree exactly with those used here, owing to different methods of estimating the mileage, and show a rather smaller rise than the Connecticut figures.

limits in Illinois say that unreasonable speed limits may cause an increase in accidents.

9. OTHER TYPES OF LIMIT

In some of the states of the U.S.A. it is the practice to use what are called *85 percentile limits*. When a limit is proposed, the traffic is timed, and the limit posted to the nearest round number to the speed which 85% of cars are not exceeding. Then, when the traffic has had time to settle down, it is again timed, and the figure altered if found necessary to comply with the 85%, even if this change is upwards, and this process may be repeated as necessary.

This means that the more responsible drivers fix the limit. The idea behind it is that *at least* 90% of drivers are reasonable, responsible people who can be trusted to drive at a safe speed. The figure of 85% is then on the safe side. It is argued that if the more responsible section of drivers has set the limit, the remainder will realize that it is reasonable. It is claimed that timings of traffic confirm this, and that remarkable reductions in accidents have been made by such limits. It certainly does seem to be a reasonable way of doing things, and much better than our way of letting the limit be decided by the local busybody.*

In parts of the U.S.A. the limits are not made absolute such as ours are, but *prima facie* or *advisory*. That is, a driver can exceed the limit, but if he does so and has an accident, he is considered to be responsible unless he can prove to the contrary. If he was below the limit, his responsibility has to be proved. In 1948 more than half the U.S.A. used this type of limit, often combined with the 85 percentile principle, but the proportion has been falling, largely, I understand, on police influence. This type of limit is much more difficult to enforce, and enforcement is, of course, much more important than saving life.

I think there is much to be said for this advisory limit. It puts the driver in a position of trust, and leaves him with some room for discretion. At certain times exceeding a posted limit may not be

---

* This is not just a bit of sarcasm. *It is the ghastly truth.* I speak from much experience, and instances of it can be seen frequently in our local press. To do them great credit, the Ministry are now doing their best to stop this kind of thing, not always with success.

dangerous, and then an absolute limit becomes merely prohibition for the sake of prohibition. Also, if a posted limit is strictly obeyed, it will reduce traffic to speeds much below the nominal limit, and even cause long queues, by making it difficult or impossible to pass slower vehicles. This, in its turn, may very likely produce more accidents.

10. TIMINGS OF TRAFFIC

It was for some years the practice to time traffic in Dorset either where a limit had been demanded, or on similar stretches of road. We had a technique of timing which was not obvious to drivers, and which compared in accuracy very reasonably with the police radar meters.

In these timings, only vehicles which had complete freedom to use what speed the driver wished were timed. Those which were held up in any way were disregarded. We wanted to find out the mean speed, and the range of speed, that traffic would use if it had complete freedom.

The analysis of these timings is given, in some detail, in my book on statistical methods.* The conclusion from the study was that a posted limit made very little difference to the speeds, but that the general road conditions did make a large difference. *If it could be said that there was no doubt that a speed over 30 mile/h was dangerous, then no driver was ever doing that speed.* As the probable safe speed increased, so did the speed used, but even then the number of high speeds recorded was small. Out of nearly 2,500 cars timed, none was doing over 60. Five were doing between 50 and 60, and less than 4% of the total were doing over 48 mile/h.

There was, of course, much variation in the speeds, the range being between 12 and 60 mile/h. The general conclusion from the timings was that, with the exception of a tiny minority, the traffic adjusted its speed to the conditions of the road, while a posted limit made little difference. It hardly altered the mean and median speeds compared with those when there was no limit, though there did seem to be some *slight* tendency for the faster drivers to reduce their speed a little. This has been observed in other timings in this country and in the U.S.A. My own sample was a very large one,

---

* See Appendix, p. 223.

combining a large number of timings in different places. Here, again, there is little or no evidence to support Mrs Castle's statement that speed limits markedly reduce speeds.

It is even sometimes found that drivers increase their speed after the posting of a limit. This was not shown in my 30 mile/h study, possibly because the mean speed was already over the speed limit, but it was shown dramatically, and rather tragically, in a 40 mile/h limit posted in Dorset. This was done after strong local agitation, and I had always opposed it. After the posting, timings showed that the modal group of traffic had gone up from the 30–32 mile/h group to the 38–40* mile/h group, although the mean and median speeds were unaltered. This clearly showed that many drivers had increased their speed after the posting of the limit.

Before the limit, there had not been one fatality on the stretch of road subject to it, though the records went back nearly twenty years. After it was posted in July 1962 there was one in 1963, and two in 1964. In the three years before the posting of the limit there were 16 injury accidents on the length—including 7 serious and one fatal—and in the three years after posting, there were 30 injury accidents—including 14 serious and 3 fatal. Whether this rise in accidents is due to the increase in the modal speed is anybody's guess. There were no noticeable changes in other factors at the site, and no reason to suspect any large increase in traffic. The possibility that the increase in fatal accidents was fortuitous is reduced by the fact that similar increases have been observed at other sites.

Fortunately, the tendency to drive up to the limit has not been marked on the motorways so far.

11. WHY ARE SPEED LIMITS NOT MORE SUCCESSFUL?

Speed limits are not conspicuously successful. The only significant reductions caused by them are in the 50 mile/h limit in reducing all accidents, and possibly, serious ones, although it may have increased fatal accidents. In general, it seems that they are more successful—perhaps less unsuccessful would be a better way of putting it—in reducing minor accidents than serious and fatal, particularly fatal.

---

* In this case, owing to the interest of the study, the timings were taken in groups of 2 mile/h, not in the 4 mile/h groups mentioned on p. 10.

We can say with confidence that the driver is very frequently not wholly responsible for the accidents. It is therefore possible that the exaggerated claims made for speed limits may lead other road-users to be less careful after the posting of the limit, thinking that all is now well, and that the place has been made quite safe. The same remark may apply to other motorists entering the road from side turnings.

Another possibility is that the limit may upset the random spacings of the cars, making the gaps between them more regular, and so giving pedestrians fewer gaps in which to cross the road.

It is often argued that if the 30 mile/h limit was strictly observed—which it certainly is not at present—the accidents would fall dramatically. One book was even written to 'prove' that if this was done, the deaths would fall to half. There is nothing to support such a conclusion. An examination of accident maps of any town will show that most of the accidents occur in the streets in which speeds are almost certainly much below 30. In the Birmingham study (BIR.4) which was made mostly in residential parts of the city where speeds would be expected to be higher than in the more congested areas, it was concluded that most of the accidents took place at less than the limit speed. The relaxation of 30 limits to 40 does not increase accidents (line 18 of Table 10, p. 46).

In a recent study by the RRL* of the enforcement of the limit in several parts of the country it was found that speeds were reduced, and that accidents fell by 25%, though the report says that this was not necessarily due to the reduction in speed, but might be due to the presence of the police improving road-user behaviour—in all road-users of course. The report also goes on to say that the extra cost of the police necessary to enforce the limit would be greater than the benefit in the cost of the accidents saved. This—which may sound sordid—merely means that there might be other ways of spending the same amount of money which would produce a greater saving in accidents, such as pedestrian guard rails, pedestrian traffic lights, or improvements to junctions or surfaces.

The report made its estimate of the saving in accidents by taking

---

* J. M. Munden, 'An Experiment in Enforcing the 30 mile/h Speed Limit'. RRL, Report No. 24. RRL, 1966.

six sites, but only used five. There was one at which there was a 50% *increase* in accidents, and this was left out of the sample on grounds of unusual circumstances. I feel a little doubtful as to the propriety of this, and have not done it in my own samples which, as I have already explained (p. 48), include all the sites sent in. This experiment, then, is hardly conclusive, and one can fairly confidently reject the theory that enforcement of limits would materially reduce accidents.

We might make speed limits more effective by posting them on the 85 percentile principle, and by making them advisory. They would then command the respect of the majority of drivers, which they very definitely do not now. If they really commanded respect, they would then become self-enforcing. Timings show very clearly that drivers adjust their speed to the conditions, quite regardless of whether a limit is posted or not.

12. 'THE CAUSE OF ACCIDENTS IS SPEED'

This is a statement often made, and the idea behind it is no doubt the basis of most of the demands for speed limits.

But what does it mean? What is speed? Its scientific meaning is merely motion. A snail has 'speed', and so has light, but expressed in units these are rather different. If this definition is used the statement is a truism. If we eliminated speed by rooting everything to the ground, there would be no accidents, but only because in a short time there would be no one to have accidents, because speed is essential to life and we would die without it.

If we amend the statement to mean 'high speed' we are still in difficulties. What is high speed? Our ancestors thought that twenty miles an hour, which we now think a crawl, was high speed. Some of them even 'proved' that a speed of 30 miles an hour was lethal in itself, and that no one could live at that speed.

It all depends on circumstances. A speed which would be a crawl—almost dangerously so—on a motorway, would be lethal in Oxford Street in the shopping hours. Our ancestors, with their twenty miles an hour maximum, killed more people in travel accidents, relatively, than we do (Table 3, p. 22).

If we then change the term to 'speed too high for the circumstances' we are still in difficulties. The circumstances can alter in a tiny fraction of a second for reasons beyond the driver's control. He may be doing a reasonable speed, but if a pedestrian dashes out from behind some obstacle, his speed has become too fast for the circumstances, *although in such a case, it is really the pedestrian who is travelling too fast for the circumstances, though few would admit this.*

The more we analyse it, the more foolish does this statement appear. But some very astonishing calculations have been made of the number of accidents we could save by limiting speed. Goen, in the U.S.A., said that 'fatalities are proportional to the cube of the speed', and worked out that we could get a 44% reduction in deaths from a 20% reduction in speed. This would presumably mean that the deaths on a motorway, in proportion to mileage, would be two hundred times those in a shopping street. We see from Table 4 (p. 23) that they are about one-twentieth of them. Table 10 (p. 46) shows that in fact some of the works which *reduce* accidents *increase* speed, and that these works often reduce fatal accidents more than minor ones, while those which reduce speed, such as speed limits, seem to increase fatal accidents more than minor ones. This is what I meant by the apparently astounding statement on page xiii that I had spent my life increasing the speed of traffic to reduce accidents.

The idea that speed is the cause of accidents has its dangerous side. It may very likely be that the people who dawdle on crowded trunk routes, and cause so much frustration and congestion, think that they are being safe, and that they contribute to safety by making other 'road-hogs' slow down, but they are really the road-hogs themselves, by causing danger, and being grossly inconsiderate. It is said that drivers should not get frustrated, and should be patient, but it is nerve-racking dawdling along in queues, and is also dangerous. It is hard to blame the father of a family for getting frustrated and impatient when he is taking them down on holiday to Cornwall, and crawling down that dreadful country lane A30/A303 in procession behind a dawdler with his children repeating endlessly: 'When are we going to get to Trepolpen?'

8

SIGNS

'An evil and adulterous generation seeketh after a sign'
Matthew, 16, verse 4

1. THE POPULAR SUPERSTITION

The public is very superstitious on the subject of signs. As soon as there is an accident, someone says 'Put up a sign!' Juries, Councils, Road Safety Committees, everyone says so. They seem to think that there is a sort of magic charm, or a radar set, in a sign, which automatically makes the driver slow down—itself of course the one single infallible remedy for all accidents—and so makes things safe. Many times, when I have had requests for signs from some such body as I have mentioned I have asked what sign would be appropriate, they have answered: 'Oh, any sign will do, to make the motorist slow down!' One bright soul even suggested that I put a school sign at a bend miles from any school.

Yet the most extraordinary thing is that these people do not see the signs when they are there. I began to keep a record of the number of times some such person asked me for signs which were already there, but gave it up, it happened so often. One of the most amusing cases of this kind of thing was a ferocious letter I got from a Parish Council saying: 'On whose authority have all the school signs in the village been taken down? Put them up again at once, or else ...!' Nobody on my staff knew anything about it, so, happening to be near the village, I went and looked. All the signs were there, and the bolts holding them to their posts were solid with rust. They had never been moved since they were first put up. When I asked the Parish Council what they meant, I got no answer.

I had a blast from a well-known lady asking furiously why there was no school sign in the village 'to protect the children'. My answer was: 'Madam, if you will go to your dining-room window, and look slightly to the right, you will see the sign. It has been there for fifteen years.' I did get an amused reply and all was well. But I could fill the book with such stories. How does one account for things like this?

2. 'WOLF!'

Early in my motoring career, I had a largish car made in the early twenties, with brakes that were purely symbolic, so I had to rely on the gears on hills. Touring in the West—not, I am glad to say, in Dorset—I saw a steep hill sign and dutifully changed down, but found only the slightest of knaps.* Then the same thing happened again, a steep hill sign at a knap. The third time I saw it I said to myself that 'steep hills don't mean anything in these 'ere parts,' and didn't change down. There *was* a steep hill with a sharp bend on it! I only just made it.

This is happening all over the country. It is littered with assorted ironmongery meaning little or nothing or much, like Gilbert's look of despair, and the motorist naturally—and rightly—pays no attention to it.

On the Great North Road, when it was being given dual carriageways, the contractor doing the work, which was alongside the existing road, had put up signs at about 100 yard intervals, SLOW, DEAD SLOW, DANGER, GREAT DANGER, and so on. The traffic—cars and lorries mixed—was batting along in procession at about 40 quite happily and safely. On a fast road, I came to a sign SLOW DOWN TO 15 M.P.H. where the construction of a motorway crossed the road. I slowed down to 40, and prepared to slow down more. But it was quite unnecessary, that speed was quite safe.

There are all sorts of other foolishnesses and absurdities on the roads. On a second-class road, just before it crossed a trunk road, I came across a Clearway sign, meaning that it was illegal to halt on the carriageway. A few yards farther on there was a Halt sign, meaning that it was illegal *not* to halt on the carriageway. I realize what was meant, but it looks foolish.

It is a common practice to put SLOW on the carriageway without telling the motorist why he is to slow down, or what is the danger. I know this is against the regulations, but they are not enforced. But this would be deceptive if the driver took any notice of it. He might easily mistake something else for the danger, and so not be ready for the real one when it comes.

Then there is that most sacrosanct of all sacred cows, the School

---

* The Dorset word for a slight rise.

sign. For a large part of the time this merely means no more than that there is a building of a certain type there. The only time it matters is when the children are going into or coming out of the school. At other times it means nothing.

At roundabouts and suchlike places, we see signs REDUCE SPEED NOW. What does this mean? Obviously something totally different to the driver of a twenty-ton eight-wheeler, doing 20 or 30, or to the dear old lady—either sex—doing a stately 35 in the fast lane, decorously cursing the driver of the Jaguar behind, wanting to do 70, and hooting at her, or to the same Jaguar driver when the old lady is not there.

Halt signs were often put up without taking the least care to see whether it was really necessary to halt. The local busybody wanted one, that was enough. There was one near where I live which illustrates the point. The side road from Buckfast Abbey, used by a large number of cars and coaches during the summer, enters the main Exeter-Plymouth Road A38, near Dart Bridge. The situation is shown diagrammatically in Figure 13, which is

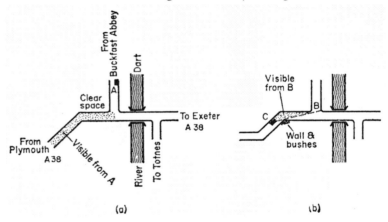

FIGURE 13 Devon, England.
Diagrammatic plan of junction at Dart Bridge on A38

not to scale. When approaching the main road, and at A about 100 feet from it, one can see a reasonable distance towards Plymouth, and tell if the road is clear, as shown in part (a) of

Figure 13. If the main road is clear, a prudent driver would then drive into the main road without stopping, and he would be safe in doing so. But there used to be a Halt sign, so he had to stop at the edge of the main road. Then, as shown in part (b) of Figure 13 his view along the Plymouth Road was obstructed by a wall and bushes, so he could only see a short way along it. The delay caused by his stopping and starting again gave time for a car coming from Plymouth direction to get to point C on the diagram before the driver at B could see him. This was near enough to create an accident situation. That there were no accidents here is a tribute to the motorist's care. The law had done its best to create them, but the motorist refused to play. There is a GIVE WAY sign now, the bushes have been cut, and all is in order. This kind of thing is common all over the country, and again I could fill the book with similar cases.

It may seem that I am abusing my own profession, because we put up the signs. But we are only advisory, and have no real power. If the Road Safety Committee, the Councils, the Ministry, do not take our advice, we can do nothing except put the sign up and take the blame. In fairness, I must say that these bodies are themselves under great pressure from the busybodies and the public. The evil and adulterous generation does love its signs, and we are in a mess.

Dare I suggest that the reason behind all this is the wish to 'pass the buck'? We have put up the sign, and all responsibility is passed to the motorist. *I have* put a danger on the road, *you* must take care.

3. THE PROPER USE OF SIGNS

It is surely obvious that the proper use of signs is that they should be clear in themselves, should convey an unmistakable message to the driver, tell him exactly what the trouble is and, finally, that they should *never* be put up except where there is a real danger that he cannot see for himself. He can then have confidence in them, and take action in that confidence. The warning they should convey is to take such action as a prudent and experienced driver would take of his own accord. The Halt sign near Buckfast Abbey offended against this principle in that it compelled a driver to take an action which was the last thing a prudent driver would have done of his own accord, and so it taught bad driving.

Also, and there is much in this, the erection of most danger signs should be looked upon as an admission of negligence on the part of the Highway Authority.

All this is not quite so easy in practice as it sounds, but with a more common-sense approach to the whole subject, much more could be done. Thus the present REDUCE SPEED NOW sign is meaningless, but if we had a more sensible attitude to speed limits, and made them 85 percentile and advisory, then we could put up a graduated series of speed signs at the approach to the roundabout, and the driver of the twenty-tonner, the dear old lady—perhaps—and the driver of the Jaguar would all know what to do, and might pay more attention to signs generally.

Then, again, the School sign. I have given cases where even the local people didn't see this. But in Dorset, the former County Road Safety Officer had the idea of putting up one which could be lighted up when the children were about, and be invisible at other times. A prototype was made in my department's Repair Depot, and put up on the outskirts of Dorchester. It told the motorist when the danger was there, and didn't warn him when there was no danger. Entirely right in principle. But it was turned down officially on grounds that seemed to me to be mere footle.

4. THE DESIGN OF SIGNS

I would not say that I am fully satisfied with the new signs. There is still room for improvement. Of course, the Ministry—in its wisdom, the wisdom of the civil servant—did not adopt the complete range of signs, and altered some of them, needless to say not for the better. Some of the prohibitory signs on the Continent, besides being circular, are 'debruised by a bendlet' as the herald says. That is to say, crossed overall by a narrow diagonal band. The bendlet has been omitted on some of ours. It is argued that the circular shape makes clear that the signs are prohibitory.

Some of the signs offend against the heraldic principle of not putting a metal on a metal or a colour on a colour. It may seem silly to suggest that we should be guided by such an out-of-date bit of foolishness as heraldry. But its principles are based on sound practical common sense. White does not show up well on yellow, or red on blue, green or black. But white or yellow show up well on the other colours, and vice versa. This remains as sound now as in the thirteenth century. The medieval knight was like a modern tank, fully encased in armour, and he depended on the heraldry to be able to tell friend from foe, so it had to be clear even when the arms were faded and torn from campaigning. A mistake due to a failure of recognition may have made a decisive change in English history. At the Battle of Barnet in 1471, the right wing of the Lancastrian Army mistook, in a fog, the mullet—five-pointed star—of the Earl of Oxford, their own supporter, for the Sun in Splendour badge of King Edward IV's men, and thought they were being outflanked. In the resulting confusion, the Lancastrians lost the battle.

Some of our signs, the No Parking and Clearway, offend against this principle, and they do not show up well.

There is much to be said for following heraldic principles, and also for using the bendlet combined with the circular sign for prohibition. Why not make assurance doubly sure? A minor difficulty is that the black bend on white in a circle has been so universally adopted to mean the reverse of prohibition, the end of a speed limit, but that could stay. Everyone has got used to it, and it has become international.

In passing, I might mention that the herald would describe this sign as 'Argent a bend sinister sable', and, except for the circular shape, the whole sign is completely described. But there is a popular association of the 'Bar sinister'* with illegitimacy. I have often wondered, perhaps a little frivolously, whether the original designer of the sign knew heraldry, and was having a dig at the motorist's parentage when he designed it.

The habit of foreign touring is growing at such a rate that I feel there ought to be a Committee of the United Nations to standardize signs internationally. At present Europe uses one set, and the U.S.A. another. Thus the European STOP sign is circular

---

* A 'bar' is a *horizontal* stripe, and so can have no hand. Sinister means the left of the *wearer* of the arms. A bend sinister would slope from the wearer's left shoulder to his right hip. The mark of bastardy should be a bend, or bendlet, sinister, though it is very doubtful whether it was really used to denote illegitimacy.

—red on white—while that in the U.S.A. is octagonal white on red or black on yellow. The American signs are perhaps better than the European.

5. DIRECTION SIGNS

Direction signs may not seem relevant to accidents, but they may play some part. People often blast off at other drivers and say that lane discipline in this country is shocking. It is no worse than in most other countries, but one does often see drivers—possibly including oneself—in the wrong lane, or in doubt about the right lane to be in. This may very likely be due to confusing direction signs, and it may make for accidents occasionally.

It is a very difficult problem, and it may be more difficult in this overcrowded country than in most others. Direction signs must be brief. One cannot put signs for Ryme Intrinseca or Redmarley D'Abitot in Piccadilly Circus, or even in towns much closer to those delightfully named places than London. The difficulty always is that the locals, who put up the signs, know the place too well to be able to guide strangers properly, and they always think that their own town is so important that anyone who does not know his way about it is a halfwit. Instead of trying to help him, they just abuse him and call him a fool. I am inclined to think that road safety would be helped if the signs in towns could be laid out by a committee from some other town. It would need a lot of police to keep the peace while it was being done, but it would be worth it in the long run.

One cannot blame the motorist for having no sense of direction either. With some one-way street systems, one has to leave a town in a southerly direction when one wants to go north.

9

PROPAGANDA

JOHNSON. 'Sir, it will be much exaggerated in public talk; for in the first place, the common people do not accurately adapt their thoughts to the objects; nor secondly, do they accurately adapt their words to the thoughts; they do not mean to lie; but taking no pains to be exact, they give you very false accounts.'

Boswell's Life of Johnson. A.D. 1777, Aet. 68

'He that is without sin among you, let him first cast a stone at her.'

John 8, verse 7

1. WHAT IS THE VALUE OF OUR PROPAGANDA?

There is a very general idea in road-safety circles that our propaganda is saving a lot of lives. There is no evidence for this, one way or the other. It is taken for granted. The argument is that the accident rate is falling, argal our propaganda is successful. But the law makes the same claim on the same grounds. Also many others say the contrary, that our measures are *not* successful. Yer pays yer money and yer takes yer choice.

In *Kim,* Teshoo Lama—or rather his munshi—wrote 'Education is greatest blessing if of best sorts, otherwise no earthly use.' Father Victor's comment on this was 'Faith, the old man's hit the bull's eye that time,' and indeed he had. It is entirely true. We must therefore consider very carefully whether our education is really of best sorts.

2. ROUSING THE PUBLIC CONSCIENCE

One complaint often made about the propaganda is that there is not enough of it, and that we have failed to rouse the public conscience. It is said that we do not realize that the problem of road accidents is the most serious social problem we have. It may be so, but probably for quite other reasons than those usually given.

I find it very hard to accept the proposition that we have too little propaganda. Surely there is no single subject on which so much attention is lavished in the Press, the BBC, even in sermons. Every holiday the BBC announces with portentous solemnity the number of killed on the roads, the papers are full of road accidents, and indeed, the impression is given that there are no other accidents at all.

This may be part of the answer. The public is so often assailed by these horrifying figures that they have become numbed and indifferent. Too much propaganda has a dulling effect, and eventually over-reaches itself.

But I feel that there is another and more important reason. The 'mere uncounted folk'—as Kipling calls the generality of us—are not altogether the fools the propagandists take us for. We realize that there is—as usual with him—much sound sense in the words of Doctor Johnson quoted at the head of the chapter, and these words apply specially strongly to our accident propaganda. We also have a sensitive nose for humbug, and much of the propaganda is humbug. To use Professor R. W. Chambers's words from his life of Sir Thomas More—'indeed some very strange and hairy Esaus' are clamouring for the public conscience. We are bombarded with causes on which our conscience should be roused, and there is a limit to what we can absorb. Moreover, in many things the propagandists are quite remarkably selective. One matter is hammered with strong words, while another, which seems to us to be exactly similar, is passed over with silence, if not with active approval. Many of those who shout loudest even give us the impression that they think that if A shoots B, the wrongfulness or otherwise of the deed depends only on who A and B are, not on the killing. If A moves in the proper circles, and belongs to the proper party, and B to the wrong one, all is well. If it is the other way about, then it is a foul murder.

In 1967, we saw the Road Safety Act passed because so many people are horrified at the *carnage on the roads,* and also the Abortion Act. Yet many people, rightly or wrongly—I am not expressing any personal opinion—think that abortion is murder. There seems to be some inconsistency here.

We seldom or never hear anything about the other accidents, twice as numerous (Table 1, p. 19.) The public conscience need not be roused if Mum has Gran staying with her, and polishes the floor in the house so that Gran falls and dies of the injury. This is not an infrequent event, but it excites no comment. Nor is anyone troubled if Mum leaves a dustpan and brush on an unlighted part of the stairs, and Gran trips over them and falls downstairs and breaks her neck.*

But if Mum takes Gran out in the car to visit someone, and skids on a polished surface, and Gran is killed, then this becomes a matter on which our conscience should be roused. Mum is prosecuted for killing by dangerous driving and severely punished. The public conscience is then appeased, and all is well. All has been done for the best—except probably to deal with the polished surface to stop more accidents of the same sort.

Much of the propaganda even gives us the impression that road accidents are the only ones which occur. ROSPA organized a meeting to celebrate its Golden Jubilee, and as part of the proceedings a Brains Trust was broadcast by the BBC under the title STOP ACCIDENTS, but the only accidents discussed by the panel were road ones. (*Radio Times,* 1.12.66.) No hint was given by the eminent people who took part that they were only discussing a third of the accidental deaths. When the holiday accidents are announced on the BBC with such portentous solemnity, no hint is ever given that there have been other deaths in other types of accident. Only road accidents are mentioned. The Cumbernauld New Town recently announced that it was the safest town in Britain, because it had fewest *road* accidents. There might have been a holocaust of home accidents in the town, but no one counts those.

This may be part of the reason why the public conscience is not roused. The mere uncounted folk, or at any rate some of them, know that other accidents happen, so that a propaganda which they realize to be biased and one-sided does not impress them. Many also realize that when the BBC makes these announcements

---

* This is not fanciful. It is an actual example of accidents in the home, taken because it happened to be the first on the list in the 'Report of the Standing Interdepartmental Committee on Accidents in the Home' issued by the Home Office. London: HMSO, 1953.

I used this example in my earliest paper on the subject of road accidents, which was given to the South-Western Branch of the Institution of Highway Engineers in a large hotel in the south-west in 1954. Some of those who took part in the discussion rather made fun of the example. But when the audience left after the meeting, down a rather poorly lighted staircase, there, in one of the darkest corners, was a large pail of water with a mop in it. Some of the jesters apologized to me.

about the holiday accidents, these are not really special to the holiday. A similar list could be given almost any three or four days of the year chosen at random, and the figures would not be very much different.

It also may be that the public conscience *is* aroused, and people realize that in cases like Mum skidding on the polished road surface they are not without some responsibility themselves. Something should have been done about the surface. Traffic engineers have been telling the public for years—it is thirty years since Bennett first raised the subject—that the roads are full of traps and deceptions. People realize that it is true—none better than successive Ministers—but they are reluctant to spend the money. It is easier and less expensive to pass the buck to the motorist.

3. ATTITUDE TO THE DRIVER

This leads us to one feature which is common to all the propaganda, in all countries. It attributes the *whole* blame, and puts the *whole* responsibility, on the driver. This takes many forms, from insinuation and innuendo down to vitriolic abuse of the type used by Hitler and Goebbels about the Jews. It is quite commonly said that the whole responsibility for accidents rests on the driver and on no one else. All facts which tell against this idea are ruthlessly swept under the carpet. To take one instance, the fact that a proportion of the annual deaths—in the past as large as 10%—occur in accidents in which no motor vehicle is concerned, is never mentioned in the official figures, and is not given any publicity. The number of these deaths can only be found in the Registrar-General's returns. He, as a statistician, is coldly concerned with facts, and will not suppress any of them.

I will give a few quotations out of my large collection to show the general attitude:

(6) 'Dr Goodhart, who had said earlier that he disliked the death penalty because he thought it was unnecessary in the United Kingdom, declared, "No one has pointed out the obvious fact that if we hanged 15 dangerous or drunken drivers a year, we should save certainly hundreds and possibly thousands of lives a year."' (*T. 11.4.56.*)

(7) 'When will a Minister of Transport show that he is aware that bad driving is the sole cause of the majority of traffic accidents?' *Letter from Mr R. W. Crosher.* (*T. 16.7.56.*)

(8) '... speed-intoxicated drivers and too sympathetic courts were criticized by a police officer at the National Conference on speed and road accidents organized by the Pedestrians Association.' (*T. 16.4.57.*)

(9) 'But Sir David* amazingly advocates less interruption of the current daily and horrifying sacrifice of innocents to this Moloch.

'An outraged public—potential victims—demand that by considerably stern deterrents, this false and man-made God be dethroned and smashed.' *Letter from the Rev. C. P. Hines.* (*DT, 30.11.62.*)

(10) 'The first victim of the "revolutionary tribunal", as it has been aptly described, grew pale when led off the road where he had just crossed the continuous line, and confronted with the four "judges"—the Prefect of the Allier Department, M. Bunau, in full uniform, a Colonel of the Gendarmerie, a highways authority official, and a representative of a safety first organization.

'The Prefect first read out a preamble which began: "Last year lunatic drivers killed 12,500 people on the French roads, and injured more than 300,000 ... When there is an attempt at murder, one tries to disarm the murderer. On the highway, disarming the lunatic means taking away his weapons, that is to say, withdrawing his driving licence to protect the innocent."' (*G. 9.8.66.*)

(11) '... but there hasn't yet been an accident between two roads or between two stationary cars. No, the blame rests fairly and squarely on the shoulders of the motorist, and no amount of verbal smokescreen can obscure this.' *Supt. W. W. R. Fleming, Central Traffic Division, Metropolitan Police.* (*AU, 2.2.67.*)

One can only conclude from these terrible effusions that the authors, and M. le Préfet, thought that motorists are the only people responsible for road accidents. The quotations are quite typical, and help to explain why we have so many accidents.

The public has accepted this, and fully believes that the motorist is the only one responsible. Some years ago, the BBC produced a film on the treatment of road accidents at a certain hospital, once again implying that that hospital took in no other accidents than road accidents. It was said that one ambulance man brought in an

---

* Sir David Renton, Q.C., M.P., had queried whether the disqualification procedure was advisable. Since the Rev. gentleman has laid down the law on my somewhat esoteric profession, perhaps I may be allowed to turn the tables on him, and suggest that he reads and carefully considers the passage from which I have taken the quotation at the head of Chapter 1, with which he seems to be unfamiliar. Oddly enough, it is probable that Sir David was advocating the reduction of accidents, and the Rev. Mr Hines their increase.

injured pedestrian and wanted to return to beat up the *motorist responsible*. He took it for granted, as also apparently did the producers of the programme, that he was responsible. It never entered into anyone's head that the pedestrian might possibly have been responsible for his own fate by recklessly stepping out.

4. THE PROPAGANDA

It is hard to think that this perpetual abuse of the motorist is the right way of going about getting his co-operation. Far more likely is it to be the worst. It is a general trait of human nature to react in the same way as one is treated, and it is much to the motorist's credit that on the whole, he does not do this. Yet the Press is full of the kind of thing exemplified by the quotations above. Any letter which abuses the motorist seems to be sure to find space, even in such a generally sober and objective journal as *The Times,* while letters setting out the facts do not. Many times have Editors regretted their inability to publish letters setting out the facts after someone had made an outrageous statement. I even wrote to the editor of one serious journal asking him point-blank if it was editorial policy not to publish any letters which seemed to defend the motorist, and I got an evasive reply.*

The propaganda itself, apart from the abuse, is very much like the curate's egg in the old story, 'good in parts'!

On the Basingstoke Bypass, I once saw a poster by the side of the road, and as it might have had some important message for me, I took my attention off the road for a few seconds and read:

A MOMENT'S
INATTENTION
CAUSES
ACCIDENTS

Basingstoke Road Safety Committee

---

* It is only fair to put in a proviso here that there *is* one exception to this, which is the *Listener,* the journal of the BBC. *The Times* also seems less likely than most other journals to refuse letters defending the motorist.

Rising up the scale, much of the propaganda seems to me to fail because of vagueness or obscurity. At a road-safety meeting there was a display of ROSPA posters, and one read BE ALIVE TO OVER SIXTIES. What did this mean? I could not decide, and asked several people present. Some thought it meant that we should be aware of drivers over sixty, others that we should beware of pedestrians over sixty, and others that we should ourselves try to remain alive to over sixty. Propaganda of this kind is unhelpful for it causes confusion.

Too much of it is of the 'Be a good boy' kind of thing. As a father who has brought up several children, and has spent most of his life in a managerial capacity, I would say that I have never found this sort of propaganda much use. One must tell children—and adults for that matter—exactly what being a good boy means. The famous—or notorious—'Black Widow' poster offended against this principle. No one goes out intending to make some woman a widow—except possibly murderers and suicides who would not pay any attention to propaganda anyway—so most of this propaganda flows off people like water off a duck's back. Vague general exhortations to be careful are quite useless. At Warmwell Cross (6.11, p. 64) drivers fully intended to be careful, and were careful, but they were careful in a situation which did not exist, and careless, without meaning it, in the true situation. They had misjudged this owing to the trap in the layout.

Abuse of the drivers is the worst possible type of propaganda, even if it bears some resemblance to the truth, which it clearly does not. As Cardinal Newman said: 'When we would persuade others, we do not begin by treading on their toes.' Yet we tread hard and firmly on the motorist's toes, slap him in the face with a wet fish, and then expect him to co-operate. Things are said about motorists which, if they were said about Jews or Negroes, would produce an instant prosecution under the Race Relations Act.

5. PROPER PROPAGANDA

To be really effective, propaganda should be positive. Propaganda should tell a man what to do, and why he should do it, and put this into brief, simple and clear language. Any form of abuse should be avoided like the plague. Moreover, propaganda should be impartial, and not blame one individual for deeds which are not blamed in others.

Our present propaganda certainly does not conform to any of these principles. There is much which could be done to these ends. Some years ago, the RRL produced an excellent little leaflet describing the effect of slippery surfaces, in clear and non-technical language.* It was a perfect example of propaganda at its very best, but I could not get it any publicity. No one was interested. Yet, as I have shown (6.8, p. 59) this matter is one of great importance, and failure on the part of drivers—and, to be fair, I must add of engineers—to understand it is almost certainly a large factor in accidents (Table 10, line 10, p. 46).

Another example of the failure in this respect was the double white lines. When they were introduced, little real attempt was made to get them across to drivers. Large and conspicuous notices were put up at the roadsides all over the country, but in the nature of things, these could not be fully comprehensible. In conversations with drivers, I found that few people really understood them. The official policy seemed to be to bludgeon the idea into the driver's head by letting him disobey them, and then punishing him for his ignorance.

Much the same remarks apply to the new signs. There is much public ignorance of what they mean.

If the Press were to divert half the space it devotes to abuse of the motorist to his instruction, we might be able to save many accidents.

6. THE EFFECT OF ALL THIS

There are three aspects of this, the effect on the motorist, that on the public, and that on our rulers.

I cannot help feeling that the motorist has become deadened to the propaganda by its abusive and one-sided nature. He automatically distrusts it, not without justification. Even good and useful propaganda now passes him by without having any effect on him. If this is so, one way of overcoming this would be to lay off the motorist for a while and concentrate on the responsibilities of other road-users.

---

* 'Driving in Wet Weather'. DSIR, Road Research Laboratory, 1957.

The effect on the public is the greatest source of harm. Excellent work is being done by various organizations, especially ROSPA, in teaching children at schools, by the Tufty Club, and so on, but what is the use of this if the children then go home and are taught by their parents or others that their safety is the sole and entire responsibility of the motorist? By such people, for example, as the lady councillor who told my wife that I was *murdering the children* because I was opposing an unreasonable speed limit (p. 82). I have come across this kind of thing many times during my time as County Surveyor, and my colleagues have also given me examples. In many cases where parents demand a speed limit 'to protect our children' they really mean 'to save us the trouble of looking after our children'.

The BBC recently showed a film on television of a street in south London on which there had been an agitation for 'something to be done' to 'make the road safe for our children'. The film showed a mother seeing her two children off to school. She watched them out of the door and across the front garden. As soon as they had shut the gate, she turned and went indoors and closed the front door. Her responsibility for them had clearly ended, and some faceless *they* had taken over. The children were shown rushing across the road, and one was knocked down by a lorry whose driver was unable to avoid her. Then we were shown the usual crowd abusing motorists, the Council, the Ministry, everybody but themselves. Yet these people were only following to its logical conclusion the propaganda that the whole responsibility rests with the driver, because if this is true obviously no one else need take any care. It is noticeable that the most popular 'road safety' slogan is '*I'VE put a danger on the road, YOU must take care*'. I have come across innumerable cases in which it is clear that this was at the back of people's minds. Such people, for instance, as those who put a school at what they themselves say is a dangerous place, and then agitate for signs, speed limits, and so on.

This affects our rulers. Obviously again, if the whole responsibility rests with the driver, it does not matter in the least what tomfool laws we pass, or whether we leave traps in the roads, whether we do not bother to find out why accidents happen, whether, like Sweden, we change the rule of the road without bothering to study whether one rule may be safer than another. (3.9, p. 25)* All legislators all over the world say to themselves, probably subconsciously, *it does not matter what we do, if it goes wrong we can always blame it on the driver.*

7. THE HIGHWAY CODE

(12) 'In closing may I leave you with a parting thought. Have you considered what the effect would be if all motorists complied with the simple and common-sense rules contained in the Highway Code? Thousands of policemen would be released to catch criminals—advice so often given by motorists (by the way, why is it that motorists reported for serious traffic offences do not regard themselves as criminals?). Insurance companies would be forced into liquidation, garages would have to become competitive in their search for business: the so-called 'problem' of police-motoring public relations would disappear overnight: and over 7,000 people, doomed to die in road accidents each year, would be reprieved. Quite a thought, isn't it?' *Supt. W. W. R. Fleming, Central Traffic Division, Metropolitan Police. (AU, 2.2.67. See also Qu. 11, p. 103.)*

It is indeed quite a thought. If every *motorist* obeyed the Code there would be a complete end to all road accidents. No cyclist would ever run into a pedestrian, no pedestrian would ever dash out in front of a cycle or motor vehicle from behind a parked car, no child would ever run into the road to catch a ball; no young children would ever play under the wheels of a delivery van. Marvellous, but what dangerous twaddle. If instead of the word *motorists,* Mr Fleming had used the words *road-users* he might have been nearer the mark.

I do not for one moment mean to say that the Code is not good. Considering the difficulty of writing it, a wonderful job has been done, but I would not have thought that any responsible person could say that it can be anything more than a general guide to road conduct. As such it is good, but it is not always easy to apply the rules. Some are impossible to apply rigidly, and others become out of date because of changes in ideas, or as the result of further study.

---

* I am not saying that one rule of the road is necessarily better than the other. Only that no proper study seems to have been made of the effect of the change on accidents.

An example of this is Clause 46, telling the driver to make sure that there are no children or pedestrians in the area behind the car. Applied strictly, no one could move off at all. *But there is no clause in the Code telling those in charge of young children to look after them, and see that they do not crawl under vehicles.* Yet children who do this are killed occasionally.

Another glaring example is Clause 8, governing the use of pedestrian crossings by pedestrians. The courts have recently decided that this clause need not be obeyed by pedestrians, and if the motorist were to make sure that he would never be at fault on a crossing he would have to stop dead at each one, and tie the traffic of the cities up in small knots, and possibly even ruin the country. (TLR.T, 25.5.60; TLR.T, 28.10.60; G, 4.5.62.) In the last of these cases the judge said that a pedestrian had 'darted foolishly' on to the crossing, but he awarded 25% damages against a motorist who, he said, had behaved perfectly correctly. In all three cases the judges said that the motorists concerned had not been negligent. Here the law and the Code are at odds.

Then the judges have recently been casting doubts, though not apparently laying anything down, about Clause 3, which advises pedestrians to walk facing the traffic if there is no footpath.

The controversy about Clause 50—which advises motorists to use dipped headlights in built-up areas *unless the street lighting is good*—will be familiar to all. But it does mean that many towns have notices at the entrance to the town which mean in effect *Please disobey the Code.*

Clause 45, which says that there are rights of way at a roundabout has now been made out of date by new regulations.

The Clauses 77 and 78 are to some extent contradictory. No. 77 tells you not to wander from lane to lane on a motorway, while 78 tells you to keep to the left-hand lane except when overtaking. Yet if you are travelling on a two-lane motorway, at round about the mean speed of the traffic, you can hardly avoid disobeying one or other of these two clauses.

These illustrate the difficulty of drawing up such a code. Ideas change with experience, and it becomes out of date. They also show the impossibility of adopting Terrell's idea of a 'Code with teeth', unless it were adopted to make a lawyer's field day, or to increase accidents, both ends which it would achieve if adopted.

I do not mean this in any carping spirit, but Terrell's proposal does pinpoint the difficulty of laying down such a code and what pitfalls there are in it. As it stands, as a general code of advice, it is excellent, but there are two things which could much improve it. Some means must be found to revise it promptly if any clause is found to be unsound or out of date, as with Clauses 45 and 50. There must also be found some means of reconciling the Code and the law. We cannot have the two at odds. How can the motorist respect either?

There is also the matter of the repeated and complete disregard of the Code by other road-users. Terrell's proposal was apparently to make disregard of the Code by *motorists* punishable, but not that by others. Yet if the motorist sees complete disregard of the Code by others, how can he respect it? We get a sort of vicious circle here. Each makes the other despise the Code. In the cases I have quoted above the *pedestrian* had disobeyed the Code, but the *motorist was penalized*.

I feel there is much to be said for Austin's proposal that there should be separate Codes for each class of road-user.*

He is, perhaps, a bit unnecessarily scathing about the Code, though some of his suggestions are practical. But I cannot agree with his proposal that long explanations of the reasons for the Clauses should be given. Most of these are clear enough as they stand, and should not need explanation. People normally like clearness and brevity, and would pay little heed to long explanations, especially those of the obvious.

At least one of his suggestions would be impossible, that is if one is to pay any attention to such an airy trifle as truth.

> (13) '"Rule 18. Do not exceed speed limits." Surely this would be greatly reinforced if figures were quoted showing how speed limits can reduce accidents?' (*Op. cit., p. 197.*)

But as I have shown in Chapter 7 (p. 78) speed limits do not by any means always reduce accidents, and it is not impossible that they increase fatal accidents (Table 10, p. 46), so his suggestion could not be followed.

---

* Michael Austin, *Accident Black Spot.* London: Penguin Books 1966, Pelican Book No. A.820.

10

VEHICLES AND ACCIDENTS

By Dr G. M. Mackay, B.Sc., S.M., Ph.D., A.M.Inst.H.E.

I. INTRODUCTION

Motor-cars, like all pieces of furniture, we take for granted. It seems obvious that they should have wheels, a motor at one end, forward facing seats, glass windows, and that they should exhaust, somewhat noisily, the combustion products of petrol and oxygen. Familiarity has dulled the magic with which we travel from A to B in such surprising comfort and rapidity. The motor-car, it should be stated quite clearly, is now the most successful and most necessary of all engineering devices.

Yet there are costs. Cars depreciate at such a rate that they are the worst investments most of us ever make. They get in each other's way. They alter the whole ecology of our environment as no other machine has done, and they injure amazing numbers of people.

At current accident rates, 40% of all vehicles will injure someone in their ten-year lifespan. One out of every fifteen vehicles will injure a pedestrian in that period. The majority of these injuries will be slight. Using the standard definitions the ratios of fatal; serious; slight injury are 1 : 12 : 35. Yet in economic terms the cost is substantial. The average cost of a slight injury accident has been estimated at £175. In addition to injury accidents there are at least as many damage-only accidents, although reliable figures are very difficult to find. What is clear, however, is that in terms of the lifespan of a vehicle, road accidents are not rare, indeterminate events sprung by a malignant deity; they occur with such frequency that they are a common function of the machine. As such they must be considered as a normal event in the machine's life, rather like having an occasional puncture or subjecting the vehicle to an exceptionally heavy winter frost.

Surprisingly little is known about the ways in which accident rates vary according to vehicle characteristics. The main difficulty is that inter-relationships between driver and vehicle characteristics mask the effect of a single variable. For example, new cars (under two years old) have more accidents than old cars (over six years old) in the absolute sense, but their annual mileage is smaller. Thus, one may assume, that new cars have more accidents because they do a higher annual mileage. Old cars, one may assume, tend to be driven by younger, and perhaps inexperienced drivers, who may have more accidents regardless of the vehicle. On the other hand, old cars might be expected to have more maintenance defects and less satisfactory design of brakes or suspension which might influence their chance of having accidents. Thus the difficulties are compounded.

Still less is known when one considers different makes and models of cars. Undoubtedly different cars have different accident involvement rates. The car insurance industry bases its premiums on the idea that accident involvement varies with the power output of the engine. This, however, may well be a driver characteristic rather than a vehicular one. The cars with outstandingly good brakes, suspension and handling characteristics are the very cars which have the highest premiums attached to them.

Before discussing how vehicle factors affect accidents and injuries, it is worth describing what a road accident means in vehicular terms.

An accident is an event on the highway which leads to damage of the people or vehicles involved. In an urban environment, for example, 61% of the accidents are vehicle-to-vehicle ones, 23% are vehicle/pedestrian and 16% are single vehicle accidents which involve rollover or road furniture impacts (BIR.4). In rural areas the proportion of single vehicle accidents increases and may be as high as 40% in some of the low-density areas of the United States.

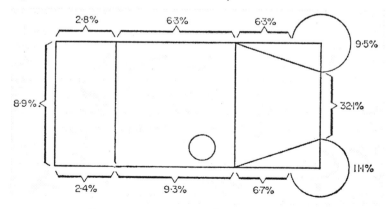

FIGURE 14 Positions of impacts on cars

Figure 14 shows the frequency with which various areas of cars are struck in urban accidents (BIR.4). Frontal impacts predominate with over 50% of the impacts in front of the front axle. These characteristics vary with the environment considered, for example, there are more frontal and less side impacts in rural areas than in cities where junctions are very common. The type of vehicle also changes the conditions; motor-cycles, for instance, have very few rear impacts.

An important but poorly understood aspect of accidents is a knowledge of the speeds of the vehicles involved. Because of the legal implications, it is unusual for a driver to say that he was travelling above 30 mile/h in a British town. To rely on independent witnesses to assess the speed of a vehicle seen or perhaps only heard for a fraction of a second while the mind is preoccupied with other thoughts, is to put a trusting but misplaced faith in human powers of observation. Many studies have shown how fallible we are when viewing the outside world through a haze of preconceptions and prejudices. How, then, can vehicle-impact speeds be estimated?

The clues available are the damage to the vehicles from impacts and the signs left at the scene, such as the length of skid marks or the damage to road furniture. A study of urban accidents in Adelaide, Australia, using environmental information in the main, showed that the mean impact speed of vehicles involved in accidents was 20·5 mile/h (the speed limit in Adelaide is 35 mile/h). Using similar procedures, but assessing vehicle damage as well, the mean relative impact speeds for vehicles in accidents in Birmingham was estimated to be 22 mile/h (BIR.4). Thus, in the absolute sense, if these studies are approximately true, accident speeds are not excessive, although they may be unreasonable for the particular circumstances. What is relevant is that road-users are seriously injured in impacts at these speeds.

There are two approaches to improving the situation. One is to improve the design of vehicles so that they are less likely to have accidents; the other is to design vehicles for having accidents without causing injury. These two aspects are now considered.

2. ACCIDENT PREVENTION

Road accidents in all their aspects are extraordinarily difficult things to study. One cannot actually see them systematically; all one can do is to pick up the pieces afterwards and try to reconstruct what happened. In one sense, accidents are only part of the total spectrum of driving risk; the accidents which do not happen are almost as important. Near-misses occur all the time, and yet to my knowledge, no research has yet been performed on these events.

It is useful to think of driving as a complex system in which a large number of variables are interacting with each other with varying degrees of dependence. Thus a critical situation may develop which would lead to an accident if it weren't for the presence of some factor such as the ability of a vehicle to round a curve at the limit of tyre adhesion. Vehicle characteristics of this sort are obviously important in pre-accident circumstances, but the influence which these characteristics have on accidents is almost completely unknown, and is one of the most important areas of research to be investigated.

With the present state of knowledge all one can do is to decide what appear to be desirable vehicle characteristics, in terms of handling, geometric design, braking systems, and so on, on the assumption that improvements in these areas will benefit the accident situation. It should be stated quite clearly, however, that improvements in the accident prevention characteristics of vehicles do not *necessarily* lead to lower involvement rates. For example, the wet road adhesion of tyres has improved greatly in recent years. This is presumably an added safety factor, and yet one result may be that drivers are more confident when cornering or braking on wet roads now, and therefore drive faster and increase the risk to the same level as before. Indeed, there is some evidence to suggest that road-users tend to drive so that in varying circumstances the 'perceived risk level' is kept constant.

This difficult area I shall leave to more esoteric publications, and describe some aspects of car design which are desirable, with the reservation that in actually preventing accidents they may not be as successful as one might think.

Sensory requirements. Vision is the most important but not the only sensory channel through which we receive information when driving. The simple geometry of car design, although now greatly improved over early post-war cars, still has blind spots at the door pillars. These areas, particularly in intersection accidents, lead to obstruction of the view of narrow objects, such as pedestrians and cyclists. Wet weather conditions especially produce blind areas for which the driver must compensate.

The height of the eyes of a driver above the road surface influences highway design considerably. It is worth pointing out that the average eye height has been decreasing in the order of half an inch per year for the last decade. Thus, roads built ten years ago have been made obsolete by a change in car design, which makes the geometry of vertical curves substandard. Until highway and car design are co-ordinated, such inefficiencies will continue to occur.

We have progressed from the days when Henry Ford said: 'You can have your car any colour you like as long as it's black.' The animal world shows us how important colour can be both as a disguise and as a signal. Bright yellows and oranges are colours most easily perceived, yet if all cars were the same colour, we would lose the value of contrast. It is likely that car colour influences accidents, but we do not know to what extent and we do not know the optimum colour-mix. Surely a good subject for a university thesis.

Vehicle lighting introduces an additional parameter into the vision system which is of great importance in the night accident situation. The relative contributions of street lighting and vehicle lighting to the illumination of the road environment are usually considered separately. It would seem reasonable to suggest that neither system can be optimized in isolation, but as yet there is little work relating the two systems together.

Headlamps are a compromise between two conflicting requirements. The driver must see the road in front, but other road-users must not suffer from glare. Glare, however, may arise in two ways, either because the approaching headlamps are too bright or incorrectly aimed, or because the car whose driver is suffering from glare has insufficient illumination of its own.

European, British and American practices in headlamp design are considerably different. There is still a need for fundamental work to establish criteria for full and dipped beam illumination, and for the best relationships between these two conditions, and the background lighting of the road scene. An important factor is the recovery of the human eye from glare. Also design and maintenance factors affect the setting of beams—in practice light commercial vehicles are particularly liable to cause dazzle with varying loads.

Sound is a minor sensory channel through which we get information of the driving situation, although totally deaf drivers seem to manage satisfactorily without it as they have no more accidents than normal drivers. Presumably horns are totally beneficial, but vehicle noise has both good and bad aspects. Good because other road-users are warned of a vehicle presence, bad because noise induces fatigue and may obscure outside sounds from attracting the driver's attention.

Comfort and layout factors. A lesson learnt early in aviation, but still being learnt in car design, is that to work a machine effectively for hours at a time, it is essential that the operator—be he pilot, driver, or housewife—is positioned comfortably and is in an acceptable atmosphere. The car accessory trade, with its booming success in gear-lever extensions, headrests, flasher switches, bucket seats, lower seat-mountings, wing-mirrors, and so on, cannot be explained away entirely by our longing for individuality and status, or the inherent gadget mania which attacks so many of us.

In a pioneering research project on the subject, Professor McFarland and his team at Harvard University analysed human factors in the design of trucks. Part of the work examined human body size in relation to the performance of control functions in the vehicles. The team showed, for example, that certain sized drivers in some vehicles could not apply the brake pedal without first changing gear (in left-hand drive vehicles).

The studies showed the need for the driving space to be adjustable so that different body sizes may fit comfortably and be within adequate reach of all the controls. As McFarland put it: 'The modern vehicle must not become a Procrustean bed, where the long and the short are expected to shrink or expand into the current available space, or avoid vehicles altogether when they can do neither.'

It is useful to think of the instruments and controls of a vehicle as extensions to the sensory and motor nervous systems of the driver. In an accident it is likely that a failure has resulted not from a simple human error but from a breakdown of the driver/vehicle system. Sir Henry Royce once said: 'If you give a man a poor tool to work with, and he comes to disaster, don't blame the man, blame the designer.'

Car accidents are undoubtedly influenced by these layout factors. This influence may occasionally be direct; as when confusion over a control produces a wrong action. At night in many cars, it is easy to extinguish the headlights when the intention is to switch on the windscreen wipers. In isolated incidences such action has led to disaster. More often, however, the influence of poor ergonomics is indirect. Uncomfortable seating, excessive pedal pressures, awkward control movements, shiny instruments, too bright facia lights, all increase the demands made on a driver. Fatigue is induced by this bad design which, in turn, leads to a reduced performance and, it may be suggested, to a considerable number of accidents. An example of bad design is shown in Plate 2 where a female driver (height 5ft. 2in.) cannot reach the controls properly while sitting in the normal driving position wearing a seat-belt.

The general environment in which a machine operator works influences his performance over a period of time, a lesson learnt early in aviation. The amount of noise and vibration, the temperature, humidity, CO_2 and CO contents, and the rate of air circulation, all affect our efficiency and are all controlled by the design of the motor-car. Carbon monoxide is known to be of particular importance because of its insidious and unnoticed action, and because the concentrations of the gas in busy urban streets, in summertime, can be several orders of magnitude greater than would be tolerated in aviation. One might even suggest that in cities most drivers are in a slightly poisoned state almost all the time. Information on carbon monoxide poisoning is hard to come by and its influence on accidents is quite unknown. All that can be said at the moment is that familiarity has bred a tolerance of a situation the seriousness of which we are just beginning to understand.

Vehicle handling. The tyre/road interface is the governing factor in the movements of a car on the highway. Suspension and braking characteristics, however, govern the forces applied at this interface.

The ideal characteristics of a car in terms of the weight distribution, wheel geometry, suspension stiffness, the positions of the axle roll centres and other design properties, are well understood. Practical reasons may cause designs to deviate from the ideal. Indeed all machine design of this nature is a compromise. But there is some evidence to suggest that the more extreme designs have an influence on accidents. The research at Birmingham University has shown that three-wheeled vehicles are at least three times more likely to roll over if they are involved in an accident than four-wheeled vehicles. Work in Australia has suggested that Volkswagens may be involved more frequently in accidents where the handling characteristics are critical. This make of car has inherent oversteering characteristics which are corrected by differential tyre pressures. The Hillman Imp and some other rear-engine cars also have this property.

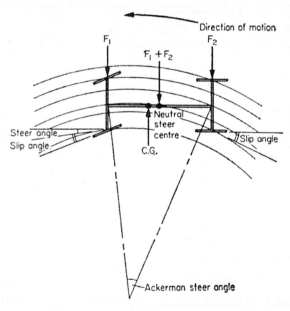

FIGURE 15 The geometry of understeer

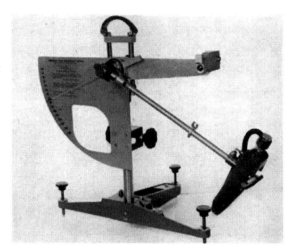

PLATE 1 Photograph of
RRL skid-resistance
tester
(*Photograph kindly supplied by
the Director of Road Research*)

PLATE 2 Poor interior design

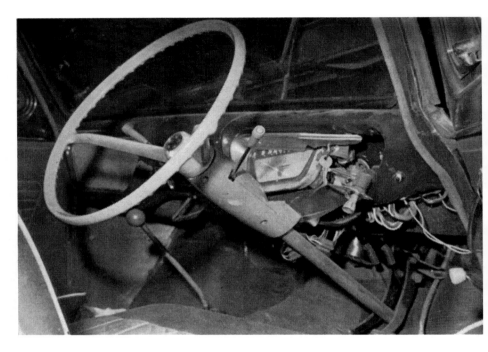

PLATE 3 Instrument panel damage

PLATE 4 Side penetration

PLATE 5 A pedestrian impact situation

PLATE 6 'The sentence may seem excessive, but something has to be done to protect the law-abiding citizen from the motorist.'

Figure 15 shows the geometry of the understeering condition. The side thrust forces F_1 and F_2 can be combined into one force which acts at the neutral steer centre, and in this case lies aft of the centre of gravity (CG). Thus if the required side force at the front axle is less than that mobilized for a given slip angle, the vehicle will follow a path of greater radius until the reduced centrifugal force acting through the CG balances the side-thrust forces. This is understeer. If, on the other hand, the CG is behind the neutral steer centre, then unless the steering is adjusted to reduce the front side-thrust, the vehicle will follow a smaller radius path. This is oversteer, and is dynamically unstable in that a vehicle, if not continually corrected back to a straight path, will seek to follow a curve of diminishing radius. The following factors affect the positions of the CG and the neutral steer centre, and thus the over/understeer characteristics of a car:

(*a*) The weight distribution between front and rear axles.
(*b*) The weight transfer due to speed changes in a corner.
(*c*) The suspension geometry.
(*d*) The suspension damping.
(*e*) Differential tyre pressures.

From the accident standpoint, all of the above factors except suspension geometry are likely to deviate from their optimum condition during the life of the car. For example, a heavy load in the rear may alter the driving characteristics from under to oversteer. Shock-absorber deterioration reduces the contact of the wheels with the road surface which, if occurring differentially, may change the handling. Variations of tyre pressures similarly change the cornering properties. For normal driving, slight understeering is desirable at low speeds. This condition may change to neutral steering around the vehicle's maximum speed, but for normal road use oversteering is to be avoided.

All of these comments on handling so far refer to a car rounding a corner under free-rolling conditions. In practice, braking is usually the overriding factor governing the forces at the tyre/road interface. From the point of view of accidents, the braking system is perhaps the most important factor controlling a vehicle's movements at critical times.

The shortest possible braking distances are obtained not when the wheels are completely locked but when they are restrained from rotating freely. This is called a state of slip and is usually expressed as a percentage. Thus 5% slip means that while the vehicle travels 100 feet, the braked wheel revolves only enough to roll 95 feet. The tyres take up the remaining 5 feet by distortion or slipping. Clearly, zero slip implies free rotation and 100% slip implies that the wheels are completely locked. The maximum retarding force is obtained for most tyres and road surfaces at approximately 10% slip.

Braking systems currently in use do not allow this situation to be exploited to the full. Under actual emergency conditions, locked-wheel braking is almost impossible to avoid. Besides reducing the retardation from its peak value, locking the wheels leads to loss of directional control. A system has been developed which overcomes this drawback. This is an anti-skid device, which has been used for many years in aircraft practice, but is not yet available on any production road vehicles except the Jensen.

The second property of the hydraulic braking system is that for a given pedal pressure, the braking force acting on each wheel is fixed. Between the pair of wheels on each axle there is usually a compensatory hydraulic circuit to equalize the pressures arising from the master-cylinder. Between front and rear axles, there is a fixed distribution, set by design, which apportions the brake effort between the two axles. This latter condition, known as the brake distribution, is defined as the proportion of the effort which is taken by the front and rear pair of wheels respectively.

For most modern cars, this brake distribution is fixed at approximately 65% on the front wheels, and 35% on the rear. This figure is a compromise between the conflicting requirements of various road surfaces. Different frictional coefficients require different values of the brake distribution if all four wheels are to be brought to the point of skidding simultaneously—the condition at which maximum retardation is achieved in practice.

Some devices are available which limit the build-up of hydraulic pressure to the rear wheels and under normal surface conditions reduce the risk of rear-wheel locking which can lead to complete loss of control and spinning of the vehicle. But, in general, it is fair to say that with current braking systems there is a considerable gap between the actual and the theoretically desirable conditions.

Tyres have the final say in the control of a car's movements on the road. Steering, suspension and brakes allow the driver to apply forces at the tyre/road interface, but it is the ability of the tyres to cope with these forces which decides what the car will do.

Great advances have been made in the last ten years in tyre design, particularly with the advent of synthetic rubbers, which allow relatively hard materials with high hysteresis losses to be used. A tyre must absorb a large amount of energy when a car brakes, and, if skidding occurs, the situation is critical. High hysteresis rubber gives shorter stopping distances on all except smooth surfaces.

Tread patterns are present to cope with wet weather conditions. At speeds greater than 60 m.p.h. the tyre contact area becomes smaller than it is at rest. Indeed, if water is present, all contact can be lost, the wheels riding on a thin film of water, and 'aquaplaning' occurs. Tread patterns influence the drainage of the contact area, and so inhibit the onset of this planing situation. No systematic work has been done to show what part aquaplaning has in accidents. It is an occasional feature of high-speed driving, but very difficult to investigate in actual accidents as no direct evidence is left and the driver may no longer be concerned with earthly matters.

Tyre pressures are a variable useful to the designer in controlling a car's handling characteristics, but they also may act very detrimentally on a car's performance. Each make and model of car and type of tyre has its own optimum pressure settings. But in practice this situation is poorly understood and is compounded by inaccuracies in the pressure gauges in garages.

In general it may be said that the modern tyre is an efficient and highly engineered mechanism. It is prevented from performing at its maximum potential, however, by braking-system limitations discussed above, and by maintenance deficiencies in operation.

With all these vehicle handling aspects, it is extremely difficult to say what effect these properties have on accidents, because of the multitude of other factors, especially environmental and road-user ones, which mask the more subtle vehicle characteristics. Until road accidents are investigated with the same thoroughness and detachment applied at rail- and air-crash inquiries, we shall never know what part vehicle factors, be they design or operational ones, have on this traumatic epidemic which is now flourishing in all developed countries.

What we do know is that accidents are a common feature of a vehicle's operation. Accident prevention is only half the story. Even if the vehicle is ergonomically perfect, with the best cornering ability, brakes, tyres and suspension that human ingenuity can devise, vehicles will still have accidents. Thus we come to the most important aspect of road vehicles, their performance in collisions.

3. INJURY PREVENTION
'It's not speed which kills—it's the sudden stop.'

A. L. Moseley

Crashworthiness as a design principle is a new idea in motor-cars. Yet, paradoxically, it is the one aspect of road accidents which is the most predictable. We cannot say who precisely will be killed next, nor specify the site at which death will occur; but what we can be certain about is that the agent will be a road vehicle. Death will occur because a human body will strike components of that vehicle, the steering-wheel perhaps, or the windscreen, with a force greater than the strength of the tissues of that body, causing injury and death.

At first sight, perhaps, these forces may seem quite unpredictable, and yet so large that nothing can be done. In fact, however, if packaged properly, the body is able to survive extremely severe forces. The pioneering work to establish how much the body can take was performed in the United States by Colonel John Paul Stapp. In connection with the space programme, Colonel Stapp and his research team built a rocket-propelled sledge which could be taken up to high speeds and brought to rest at large but carefully controlled rates of deceleration. The rider was harnessed and could be positioned in a variety of ways—spreadeagled, prone or sitting facing forwards or backwards. The most severe run was from 632 mile/h stopping in 1·4 seconds at an average deceleration of 40g (one g being the acceleration due to gravity—32·2 feet per second per second).

The aims of the work were concerned with rocket re-entry into the atmosphere and landing, but it became evident that many of the conditions being reproduced corresponded very closely to a car crash. If a car is driven into a solid barrier at 30 mile/h, the front will crumple some 18 inches to 2 feet, and the passenger compartment will be brought from 30 mile/h to rest in that distance, at an average deceleration of 30 to 40g. On the sledge these conditions were reproduced for a subject sitting facing forward—in the parlance of the sledge operators, the 'eyeballs out' ride. For these circumstances Stapp found that he could tolerate 40 to 50g with some discomfort, bruising around the harness, some stiffness of the neck and temporary shock.

Thus it was established that the *primary forces* in a car crash are not only below the levels at which death occurs, but, providing the occupants are carefully protected, the forces are below the levels of any significant injury. The trauma in actual accidents comes from the *secondary collisions,* where the occupants strike individual objects with their heads or limbs and decelerate from 30 mile/h to zero, not in 2 feet, but in an inch or two, under very localized forces. For these conditions, the decelerations may well be over 100g and it is forces of that magnitude which break bones and rupture blood vessels.

It is important, therefore, that vehicle interiors should be so designed that the severity of this secondary collision is reduced. The best single system at present available to achieve this is a seat-belt, preferably one which restrains the thorax as well as the hips. By this means the secondary forces can be brought down to the level of the primary ones.

Unfortunately, seat-belts require the active participation of vehicle occupants. The inherent optimism of the human race, coupled with the complexity of present belt design, which requires the user to go through the convolutions of a belly-dancer in order to find and couple the several belt ends, ensure that belt usage is confined to a small minority. In Birmingham studies have shown that less than 5% of car and light commercial vehicle drivers have belt protection in actual accidents. On motorways (where the chances of impact per mile travelled are much lower) belt usage increases, but even so, less than one quarter of drivers accept and use belts.

Bearing this in mind, it is important to discover precisely how road injuries come about. Certain aspects can be simulated in experimental work with dummies, but the main source of information is what occurs in actual collisions.

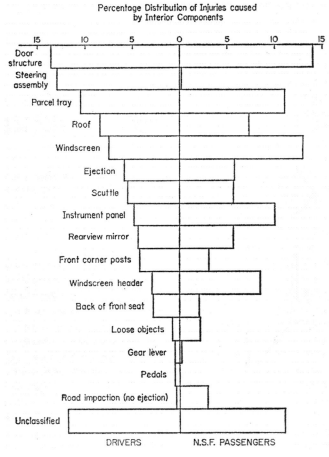

FIGURE 16 Ranking of components causing injury

Figure 16 shows the frequency with which interior components caused injury to drivers and nearside front passengers. This study emphasizes the importance of side impacts, and the door structure in generating injury.

Plates 3 and 4 show examples of vehicle interiors where injuries were caused by some of the components.

Pedestrian protection. Forty per cent of British road fatalities are pedestrians. These people are injured by striking the front of vehicles, but also by being projected from the vehicle to the road surface, where they receive secondary blows. Consider the girl in Plate 5. Imagine the car striking her at 30 miles/h as she crossed the road. The first point of contact is the bumper and her shin. She begins to rotate, striking her thigh and hip on the grill and bonnet. Her arm and shoulder then hit the horizontal part of the bonnet, and her face goes into the wiper blades and windscreen. She is now travelling at the same speed as the car, the driver of which has been able to begin braking. The car stops and she travels on at 30 m.p.h. until she hits the road surface obliquely.

Her injuries are: fractures of the tibia and fibula, extreme bruising of the thigh, hips, shoulder and arms, lacerations and facial fractures, lots of abrasions to the head and body from road surface impacts.

If the car was of a different design, the injuries would be different—for example, the high blunt radiator of the Rolls-Royce would cause very severe thoracic damage, and increase the chance of the pedestrian being projected downwards under the wheels, often with fatal consequences.

Thus there is room for improvement in the exterior design of cars, apart from the removal of the more obviously horned features. Dr Wakeland has suggested a design method, which is quoted verbatim:

(14) 'Tests beginning with local injuries and proceeding towards large-scale effects can be safely made by human subjects. The local injury sources of any vehicle might be evaluated, for example, by the person responsible for vehicle design. In effect, the responsible person puts himself in the position of the pedestrian and approves his own design, while acting as experimental subject. In such a test, the subject dons light summer clothing and attaches ropes to his wrists. He then positions himself so that, when his assistants take up tension on the ropes, the subject will be drawn slowly over the surfaces of the vehicle which he has designed. The subject is thus able to stop the test and make design correction for local injury sources when he considers changes desirable. Then he may resume the test.

'This test provides the automobile designer with a personal basis for judgement of the importance of ornaments and the need for preventing local injury. The test is completely non-hazardous. It may be called the Automobile Stylists Keel-Hauling Test after its similarity to a procedure once used in the British Navy.'

Motor-cycles. Although the car is the most important vehicle in terms of the number of injuries it generates, motor-cycles are likely to remain in considerable numbers exposing their riders to particularly high risks. The same principles of packaging car occupants apply to motor-cyclists, although the strictures of design are more severe. Motor-cyclists are better off remaining on their vehicle than being ejected, and they could well be protected, particularly against low-speed impacts, by properly engineered fairings. Chest pads could be installed to absorb forward impact forces and fairings should be extensive enough to protect the arms and legs.

4. CONCLUSIONS

From what I have been discussing it is evident that the role of the vehicle in traffic accidents is vital, complex, and not entirely understood. By definition vehicles are involved in road accidents 100 per cent of the time, so that the design aspects, particularly of cars, are extremely important. Recent legislation in the United States shows one approach—establishing Federal Design Standards to which all cars must conform. Such items as steering-column penetration, door-lock strength, seat-mountings, and seat-belt design are controlled by law, so that the cost of safety is no longer a competitive item between different makes and models.

It is likely that similar legislation will be introduced elsewhere. Indeed, the Common Market countries are already discussing international standards for safety in car design. But the American experience has also shown our lack of knowledge of the exact nature of road accidents. Because of this lack of knowledge the present Federal Standards are open to criticism as the research on which such standards must be based is not adequate yet to establish the best characteristics and to clarify the priorities involved.

Within the next decade, however, we can look forward to

substantial improvements in car design, particularly in their crashworthiness. Under the pressure of American legislation all vehicle manufacturers will have to meet increasingly stringent safety standards, and other countries are likely to follow the transatlantic lead.

In the longer term urban congestion and new propulsive units (fuel cells perhaps or high power output batteries) will radically change present vehicle concepts. More of the driving task will become automated, indeed completely automatic control on restricted roads is already feasible technically.

Safety will become a much more dominant factor because the economic drain of road accidents will become increasingly intolerable, and the social aspects increasingly unpalatable. In the highway/vehicle/road-user system which we are discussing in this book, the vehicle is a key element susceptible to great improvement if enough of us will recognize the problem and have the energy to work towards a solution.

II

THE DRIVER AS THE DOCTOR SEES HIM

By Dr K. F. M. Pole, L.R.C.P. & S.(Ed.) L.R.F.P. & S.(Glas.) M.D.(Vienna).

'...: but man, proud man,
Drest in a little brief authority,
Most ignorant of what he's most assured.'
William Shakespeare, Measure for Measure

I. INTRODUCTION

It has been said that 'there are three main factors to traffic safety—the roads, the cars and the drivers'. This is an over-simplification ignoring pedestrians, playing children, dogs and cats, apart from a variety of less frequent factors which may impair safety. However, if we accept the statement as it stands, it is right to say that medicine has a contribution to make to all of them.

Pedestrians, cyclists and passengers come within the scope of the doctor only when they have been involved in an accident and need treatment. Medical Committees have, of course, to consider them as well, so that the advice given in the eventual report will benefit all categories of road-users. However, the principal concern of the individual doctor is with the driver, and this under a three-fold set of circumstances. Firstly, he may be the driver's regular doctor, called to advise on his driving ability. Secondly, he might be concerned with the driver immediately following an accident and called upon to give first-aid, or he may be a casualty officer in a hospital rendering treatment made necessary by shock and possibly injury, or he may be called by the police—and in this case, not necessarily after an accident but because of circumstances which seemed to indicate the danger of an accident. Acting on behalf of the police, the doctor would have to pronounce on the fitness of the driver and, if he found the driving ability impaired, to certify what, in his opinion, was the cause of it. Thirdly, after a fatal accident, he may be called upon to pronounce death, or, as a pathologist, to perform a post-mortem. The doctor may also be called some time after an accident, in the course of convalescence, to assess the damage done and to give his prognosis.

The experience gained from the circumstances of accidents, and from the resulting injuries, may well enable the doctor to make a contribution to the design of cars and of various safety devices; crash helmets, collapsible steering columns, and safety harnesses are examples. Furthermore, the reconstruction of a motor accident from the injuries may elucidate responsibility. After all, it makes a lot of difference whether a cyclist or pedestrian has a heart attack, collapses in the way of a motor vehicle, and is run over being already dead, or whether he is killed by being run over. It also makes all the difference whether a driver has an accident, involving others, due to careless or dangerous driving, or whether he collapses at the wheel through natural causes, and his illness or sudden death make him lose control of the vehicle and thus cause an accident. Questions like that have an importance not only in criminal law, but might well have importance also in civil law when the question of compensation arises.

It has been estimated that the proportion of accidents due to human factors as against those caused by technical or mechanical faults is 90% against 10%. This statement is worded rather loosely in two respects. Strictly speaking, the human error accounts for practically 100%, but it is not always an error at the time of accident; some of the errors may have occurred in the design or the making of the car, the tyres or the road, or in the placing of road signs. The other more serious inexactitude lies in the word 'cause', and I fully agree with Leeming (5.1, p. 39) that rightly we can speak only of contributing factors. It would, therefore, be more correct to say that in 90% of road accidents the driver or other persons involved failed to take action which could have avoided the accident, while in only 10%, because of mechanical or technical faults (and there may be other circumstances beyond the driver's control) the persons involved had no chance to take avoiding action. Even so, the figures quoted are but an estimate.

All this having been said there is no doubt that the driver's actions are of paramount importance for safety on the road, and it is, therefore, exceedingly important to assess any impairment of the ability to drive a motor vehicle, and, in case of doubt, to review the position after a time, or even periodically. This brings us up against the problem of the granting, withholding and revoking of licences for medical reasons, and therefore to the question: what illnesses, traits or conditions should bar people from obtaining or holding a driving licence?

2. PHYSICAL DISABILITY

The main types of physical disability concern the heart and circulation, possibly with involvement of the lungs, or they affect the eyes, the metabolism of the body, the nervous system or the bones and muscles.

The first group is represented in the main by coronary heart disease, angina pectoris, serious heart diseases and high blood pressure, which might cause a 'stroke', or be accompanied by dizziness, disturbance of vision and possibly collapse as the result of drugs given for treatment. Patients with coronary artery disease and with angina pectoris—at least private motorists—almost invariably have sufficient warning of an attack to stop at the roadside, anyway under the road conditions which at present prevail in Britain. If ever we come to have five-lane traffic in this country, the position might have to be re-considered. As with most diseases, each patient has to be assessed individually, as the driver's reactions vary widely. Even in healthy people, the heart rate may rise to 120 to 140 per minute in fast-moving city traffic, particularly at busy intersections, and the electro-cardiogram(ECG) shows changes which make it clear that the response of the heart muscle to apprehension or anxiety involves something more than a simple increase in the heart rate. The connection between emotional tension and anginal pain is well known, but as drivers often may have several hundreds of such anginal pains, which can be traced back over many years, the significance of these pains to the individual as a driver must not be over-emphasized. Cases have even been quoted in which patients with acute damage to the heart muscle in consequence of coronary thrombosis have driven themselves some one hundred miles to hospital. At the same time it must be taken into account that the risk of having a secondary coronary episode has been said to be ten times as great as that of having a first.

Cases of high blood-pressure should be judged on signs and symptoms of the disease rather than on actual pressure levels. Narrowing of the main artery may sometimes lead to sudden unconsciousness, but little seems to be known about the occurrence of fatal or non-fatal accidents due to this condition. 'Hypersensitive carotid sinus reflex' (an over-sensitivity in either side of the neck to pressure, which may be caused by something as simple as a tight collar, or a heavy necklace) is another condition which may, without warning, lead to a complete black-out through the sudden fall in blood pressure, but in the literature concerned with driving I found but one single reference to this.

Lung conditions and atmospheric pollution, particularly in long-lasting traffic jams—both possibly aggravated by smoking—may result in a reduced oxygen supply to the brain, with or without retention of carbon monoxide. This may lead to drowsiness and slowing of reactions, on the one hand, and on the other to over-confidence which is in contrast to the impaired performance. Even a severe bout of coughing may cause a driver to lose adequate control of the vehicle, sometimes with complete loss of consciousness (cough syncope), and also violent sneezing can lead to impairment of the driver's vision and alertness long enough to cause danger.

Impairment of sight is one of the disabilities especially referred to in the application for a driving licence, but all that is demanded for the issue of a licence is the ability to read (with glasses if worn) at a distance of twenty-five yards in good daylight, a motor-car number plate containing six letters and figures. This stipulated requirement is equivalent to a visual acuity of 6/12 using both eyes together; but a test of vision is not compulsory, and the applicant is only recommended to seek professional advice if he is in any doubt. There is a tendency now to demand higher standards of vision, but there are other defects which are likely to be of greater importance than that of lessened visual acuity, principally a restriction of the field of vision particularly in its outer portion; compensation for this condition by moving the head and the eyes has a limited value. No mention is made of this condition in the application form for private driving licences in Britain, though there is some reference to it in that for public service vehicles. Squints may well cause a driver when he tires to misjudge distances, and in cases of latent squint fatigue may cause double vision which is particularly dangerous.

With the standardization in the positioning of traffic lights, colour blindness is of less importance than it used to be; adoption of a system used in Switzerland with the red lights showing round, the green lights showing square, and the yellow lights triangular would, however, add to safety. The danger that a colour-blind person may fail to recognize the red lights of a parked vehicle, seems to be more theoretical than practical.

Deafness, even of considerable degree, is usually quite well compensated, and generally not considered to be a substantial handicap to private motoring; even for public service vehicles no specific rules exist in Britain.

Of the diseases which affect the metabolism of the body, diabetes is the principal one to be considered. It is generally agreed that the cases which can be adequately controlled by diet alone are no special risk, nor are older individuals who can be balanced with the help of tablets. It is the patients on insulin therapy (estimated to be about 30% of the known diabetics) who present a problem, and overall even they are a very small risk; only those in whom balancing fails and who are liable to repeated collapses resulting from a sudden drop of the sugar content in the blood, should be banned from driving private motor-cars. Of course it is essential that the patients should know that 'insulin overdose' which leads to such attacks is relative, and that most commonly it comes about by having the usual dose of insulin but then delaying or omitting a meal; they must, therefore, be thoroughly instructed regarding the need for regular meals, also that unusual exercise might upset the blood sugar-insulin balance, and that, if they have any signs or symptoms of such 'hypoglycaemia', they must at once take extra glucose, of which they should always carry an emergency supply in suitable form. A diabetic driver who is found to have impaired driving ability because of such insulin-induced hypoglycaemia, is answerable in law under the Road Traffic Act as driving when under the influence of drink and/or drugs to such an extent that his driving ability is, for the time being, impaired. While almost everyone will sympathize with a sick person who, under exceptional circumstances, may thus be convicted without being morally guilty, in the vast majority of cases the responsibility is rightly his. Patients who are precariously balanced and suffering from such attacks, should have divulged this in answer to the question on their application form for a driving licence regarding 'sudden attacks of disabling giddiness or fainting'. Well-balanced diabetics, on the other hand, will hardly ever be subject to these attacks, except if thoughtlessly or recklessly—that is, through their own fault—they break their routine.

In the extremely rare case of hypoglycaemic (too low blood sugar) coma occurring in a previously well-controlled patient, without any guilt on his part, it is to be hoped that the driver will be given by the Court the benefit of 'special reason' which allows disqualification to be dispensed with. Any such case should in fairness be treated as one of illness, just as hyperglycaemia (too high blood sugar) which may occur when a patient has taken either insufficient insulin or an excessive amount of sugar or starch. The concept of insulin as a drug is anyway a doubtful one, as this substance is normally produced by the body; strictly speaking, insulin is given as a substitution therapy to some diabetics whose bodies fail to manufacture a sufficient quantity of it. Whether under the circumstances it is correct to deal with a case of insulin coma, which is induced by neglect of reasonable precautions, as 'driving under the influence of a drug' or as 'dangerous driving' is a problem for the legal expert rather than the doctor.

Other comparatively common metabolic diseases which may have significance in connection with driving ability, and therefore need medical assessment, are those affecting the thyroid gland. Overfunction (commonly known as thyreotoxicosis, 'Graves's' disease, or exophthalmic goitre) may, apart from possible eye complications, lead to excitability, and this might interfere with driving, while reduced function (myxoedema) may cause physical and mental reactions to become abnormally slow and thus present a risk. Kidney diseases may, of course, lead to metabolic disturbances.

The principal conditions which affect the organic nervous system are epilepsy and brain injuries.

According to the Road Traffic Act, persons suffering from epilepsy are excluded from holding a driving licence, and this is generally accepted as being right. 'Petit mal' (a form of epilepsy without fits but causing passing phases of consciousness being in abeyance, sometimes associated with semi-automatic movements and conditions of muscle spasms and cramps which may cause temporary paralysis of a limb) is as dangerous as 'major epilepsy' with fits. However, the idea 'once an epileptic, always an epileptic', which appears to have still been held when the World Health Organization in 1956 issued their guiding principles for the medical examination of applicants for motor vehicle driving permits, is no longer widely accepted. Thus the problem may arise when a certain individual with a history of epilepsy can be considered to be free from the disease, and the criteria to judge this have, in recent years, been much discussed.

It seems to be generally agreed that the patient who has been without an epileptic attack for five years, and of those the last two years without any anti-convulsive treatment, and whose 'EEG' (electro-encephalogram, a recording of the electrical discharges of the brain, as the electro-cardiogram is of the heart) is normal, can be considered as cured. There is, however, a large body of opinion which considers that this ruling is too strict, and certainly it is too rigid. Some changes in the EEG may remain permanently and have no significance regarding activity of the illness. Much would depend on the personality of the driver and the type of past attacks. It has even been suggested that persons who have been free from attacks for two or three years, while still taking the drugs, should be re-issued with a driving licence. This is accepted in several countries. However, in a recent case in this country where this question came up, Lord Justice Parker said: 'As long as it is necessary for a person to be under treatment for a disease or disability, then that person must be held to be suffering from that disease or disability.' This, of course, is logically correct, but an argument might well turn round the question whether the fact that treatment is given proves that treatment is still necessary. While it might make for a neat legal position, this is certainly not a cogent conclusion from the medical point of view. What about persons living in the tropics and taking quinine against a malarial attack, can they be considered to suffer from malaria? Or persons having suffered from 'endocarditis' (an inflammation of the lining of the heart which often involves the valves) in the past, who are given penicillin as an 'umbrella' for tooth extraction; they certainly cannot be said to still suffer from endocarditis. Equally incorrect is the submission that a driver taking drugs to prevent attacks would come under the proviso of the paragraph in the

Road Traffic Act which deals with driving under the influence of drugs. This paragraph applies only where the influence of the drugs is one to such an extent as to impair driving ability; but people who are suffering, or have suffered, from epilepsy are known to be totally unaffected by phenobarbitone in doses which make other people drowsy.

With regard to the consequences of brain injuries, a report from Karlsruhe in Germany states that about one-quarter of brain-injured war invalids in that district were holding driving licences. Among them no increased accident liability could be detected, although about 6% of this number had previously been certified as 100% invalid, and another equal number had claimed that they were able to travel by train only when accompanied, which meant that the companion had to be transported at State expense. From these findings it is obvious that, according to the purpose of an application, simulation and dissimulation play a great part, and this suggests the advisability of a medical examination in all cases. Certainly the fact of a brain injury in the past is not in itself a reason for refusal of a driving licence, but only when it is accompanied by attacks of unconsciousness, epilepsy or paralysis of certain kinds and degrees. This applies equally to other diseases of the brain, the spinal cord, peripheral nerves and muscles.

Similar considerations apply to conditions with skeletal involvement, whether congenital, due to injury or illness with paralysis, deformity, or loss of one or more limbs. These should be assessed by experts in the field—usually orthopaedic surgeons—and many a patient can be made safe to drive by operative treatment on bones or joints, tendons, or nerves, by invalid cars or by ordinary cars fitted with some special devices, and in some cases, just with the now widely used automatic gearbox or power steering.

Fatigue, which can be observed in the three distinct aspects of physical, mental and skill fatigue, may play some part in accidents and many illnesses make a driver more prone to fatigue than he would otherwise be. Any kind of mental activity leads to a state of fatigue which eventually enforces an involuntary rest pause. This is initially of quite a short duration, and quickly dissipates; it is not noticed by the individual concerned, but while it lasts no ordinary stimulus has a chance to reach consciousness, and no attention is therefore paid to the task in hand. These involuntary and unnoticed rest pauses are likely to account for a substantial number of accidents which are generally considered inexplicable. Repetition of identical impressions tends to increase the number and length of those rest pauses. This is what happens on straight, undeviating motorways which therefore have largely been abandoned in most modern planning. With progressive tiredness too, the 'rest pauses' get longer and more frequent.

Old age makes people liable to tire more easily, and the small rise in the total accident rate of old people, adjusted for mileage, (Fig. 3, p. 32) may be partly due to this, but probably more often to their inefficiency of perception. Hence the concern of insurance companies to obtain medical certificates for elderly drivers. The slower reaction time of those drivers is usually balanced by their experience and maturity, which largely prevents them from being involved in situations where very quick reactions are needed. It is the young drivers—extroverts rather than introverts—for whom driving is a symbol of independence, and driving at speed a symbol of masculinity (speeding is much more rare in female drivers) who have the largest number and the most serious accidents; those under twenty-one have been in the lead with motoring offences ever since 1956.

It may, of course, be argued that information is lacking on 'who drives what kind of vehicle, how many miles per year and what kinds of road and under what conditions of weather, traffic, daylight fatigue, intoxication, drug impairment, and so on'. The teenage accidents may also be due to the effect of their having just passed their driving tests, or the accident rate might go down if they had private apartments available. Circumstances may well play a greater part than any special teenage characteristic. The answer to all these questions is certainly important for a scientific analysis, but for practical purposes these arguments have little value, as many such circumstances are closely linked with adolescence. One might ask, therefore, in this context, whether seventeen is the best age at which to start driving; just then considerable personal adjustments are required in the transition from youth to adulthood, and emotional tensions are at a maximum.

3. MENTAL ILLNESS

Mental illnesses may or may not be associated with detectable changes in the brain, and especially the latter group presents peculiar difficulties as it would almost certainly escape detection by a routine medical examination. If in such a case a fatal accident occurs, the findings will give no clue, the relatives will not volunteer any information, and thus the root cause for any dangerous driving will remain unexplained. It is, therefore, impossible to ascertain what part such patients play in road accidents, but the fact that their emotional control is impeded, and they also lack insight into their condition, makes it likely that their contribution is considerable. A report from Germany says that of fifty male patients admitted to a mental hospital during the first two months of 1956, a valid driving licence was carried by eight, that is 16%. Obviously not all patients who held a licence had taken it with them to hospital, and as no special inquiries were made, the actual figure of drivers would have been even higher; certainly the figure would be higher among out-patients. Considering that to some patients speed is an irresistible lure, and that others drive recklessly under the influence of ideas of greatness or hallucinations (a number of cases are quoted) the problem assumes considerable proportions. Here certainly is a loophole in the law. The obvious solution would be to make special legal provisions for such cases together with a statutory duty for doctors to notify them. To report on patients without statutory duty is repugnant to most doctors. Moreover, in Britain in most cases of mental disease—not of a nature and degree which would make a patient liable to be detained under the Mental Health Act or subject to guardianship—a report to the Licensing Authority would not remedy the position. A case of manic-depressive psychosis for example, may well be dangerous when driving in the manic phase due to recklessness, and in the depressive phase because of the tendency to suicide; 'suicide by road accident' may after all qualify not only for insurance payment, but even for compensation. If such a patient were notified to the Licensing Authority he would be entitled to claim a driving test and—the dangerous phases being frequently very short—he would usually pass such a test without difficulty. Moreover many such patients have short-lasting and widely, often fairly regularly, spaced manic or depressive phases, and mostly the onset is gradual, so that the people around them are warned. It might therefore be considered unreasonable to deprive such patients permanently of their livelihood, when a short-term sick certificate, combined with special provisions in the law, is all that would be needed; in the interval they are usually conscientious and reliable, and may be excellent drivers. Any advice by the doctor not to drive during the dangerous phases will be ignored by the patient, because of his mental state, in which he thinks he knows best, while those suffering from physical or neurological disorders are usually very amenable to the advice of a doctor they have known and trusted as their family doctor—a plea against the depersonalization of medicine!

4. EMOTIONAL DISTURBANCES

Not only mental illnesses but even minor degrees of emotional disturbances are frequently associated with accidents; insomnia, lack of ability to concentrate, depression with loss of confidence, and unreasonable fears are frequent warning symptoms. There is no doubt that the majority of accidents happen to a rather small section of the population at risk, and this has led to the concept of accident-proneness. For the doctor it may be objected that, as the injury-accident rate is one in about 450,000 vehicle miles, it is statistically obvious that accidents must happen to a minority of drivers. However, the concept of accident-prone individuals is well established in other fields, and it would be strange if it did not apply to drivers.

From reliable observations we are informed that in 22% of industrial accidents, an improper mental attitude or personality maladjustment is the primary factor, and that general social factors play a part in as many as 80% of industrial accidents. There is certainly a significant incidence of tension-producing situations immediately prior to such accidents. Though studies on bus drivers in Belfast did not support the contention that some of them were accident-prone, it must be remembered that one would expect to find few, if any, among such a selected group of drivers. But even here it was found that any driver may have spells when he is more liable to accidents than at other times, and this fits in well with the concept of stress. This suggests the importance of personality traits, which usually can be considered more significant than initial ability, which may be acquired by practice. IQ levels above 80 seem to make no difference to driving ability, but among those with an IQ below 80 there is a steep rise to be found in the number of accidents. Tendencies to criminal behaviour are also very likely to be reflected in the accident rate. Drivers picked up for more serious motoring offences often have a criminal record in other respects. Moreover, among the criminal offences of adolescents, the theft of cars, or at least taking them away without the owner's knowledge and consent, takes a prominent place and there is little doubt that a driver in such a situation, precariously balanced between fear and aggression, must be specially prone to accidents. I am not aware of any statistics, but the state in which abandoned cars are all too frequently found, supports the theoretical assumption. Simple tests of reaction times give no clue for the identification of accident-prone drivers, and more complicated psychological tests are required to ascertain the relevant personality traits; such tests are in use in Paris for the selection of public service vehicle drivers, but in this country little use seems to be made of them. The more emotional and neurotic persons are those who tend to over-react to stress, to decline in performance, and to take longer to recover their ordinary level of performance; they are therefore accident-prone in the sense that they are likely to have accidents. It is those whom the psychological tests can pick out, but whether or not they will actually be involved in accidents will still depend to a considerable degree on chance. Even so the personality of the driver is a very important factor, and the saying that 'a man drives as he lives' contains a considerable element of truth, though it should be added that it may not be according to the steady façade presented to the world but as his wife or intimates know him to live. Moreover, it must be appreciated that this observation, though expressed in general terms, is applicable only to an average normal person, or to one who is obviously abnormal. But under certain, usually temporary, conditions of emotional stress, people may not drive as they live. This no doubt explains why any driver may be more liable to accidents at some times than at others. Such spells occur particularly when the driver is not aware of the inner conflict all too deeply hidden in his unconscious mind; he then cannot 'live it', yet—the car having become the modern acting-out instrument *par excellence*—he may express it in the way he drives. Thus it happens all too often, as an outlet whether of a permanent or temporary state of mind, that sitting behind the wheel a person's whole attitude changes as if the period of driving were not part of real life, but some stage between episodes of real life. Many think only in terms of 'other cars' not of 'other drivers', and thus forgetting all consideration assume a dangerously competitive or even aggressive attitude towards those other cars. The motor-car offers man a tremendous increase of power, and by identification it becomes the driver's own power and will which are thus multiplied. The greater this uncritical self-exaltation, the greater the irritation when it is obstructed.

5. DRUGS, HABITUATION AND ADDICTION

Drugs may alter the reactions, the behaviour and possibly the personality of men, either temporarily or permanently. This applies in some degree to the ordinary use of drugs, even more to abuse and, of course, to habituation or addiction. Sedatives and analgesics depress the central nervous system, and thus are liable to produce drowsiness. Tolerance varies greatly in individuals but side-effects of faintness and dizziness are well known and there is certainly a danger that mental alertness may be blunted. Some very nervous people may, of course, actually drive better when their excitability is lessened. Used over prolonged periods, however, the so-called tranquillizers do not produce a state of true psychological harmony, but rather one of comfortable and sometimes cheerful calm, a happy-go-lucky attitude which may amount to indifference, and is certainly not conducive to good driving. The danger is aggravated by the fact that many persons who are indefinitely on sleeping tablets, or other sedatives, are in need of them because they are basically unbalanced individuals, either impeded or impulsive, sometimes to the degree of recklessness. Anti-histaminics, which are much more widely used now the incidence of allergies has greatly increased, also antibiotics and other anti-infective agents, may cause dizziness, nausea, ringing in the ears, and impaired hearing. Again, with the development of modern drugs, patients who previously would have stayed at home, and possibly in bed, might feel well enough to venture out in their cars, and the doctor should think of warning his patients against the dangers involved. There remains the problem of self-medication, the unnecessary and uncontrolled taking of medicines by the public. Many strong-acting drugs are restricted to sale on prescription, but there are many headache tablets, cold-prevention tablets and others which may produce side-effects, dangerous to a driver if they are taken for too long, in too large quantities, or without the proper indication. A case has been reported in which a long-distance driver habitually took tablets against pains in the back of his head. After a slight road accident he was taken to hospital where some imbalance was noted, but no cause found and nothing further done. A few weeks later he was reported to the police as suspected of being drunk, when he was observed to get out of his lorry, staggering to the point of reeling. No alcohol was found in the blood when he was admitted to hospital but he was kept as an in-patient for observation and it was noted that gradually his balance returned to normal without special medication, and at the same time his headaches and the irritability which he had previously shown for a long time, disappeared. Eventually it was discovered that he had habitually taken some headache tablets in the mistaken belief that this was the only means of combating his headaches, while actually, after the initial relief, continued use aggravated the pain and caused neurological disturbances; he improved after he had been in hospital for some time without those tablets.

The case of habituation leads on to the problem of drug-addiction, which is becoming more and more prevalent. Habituation and addiction are not synonymous; habituation can be defined as psychological dependence, while addiction includes physical dependence and, consequently, withdrawal often causes severe reactions. Stimulating drugs, for example of the amphetamine group, can therefore be discontinued completely and suddenly under treatment, but the 'white drugs' (heroin, morphine, opium, cocaine), which almost invariably cause true addiction, have to be tapered off gradually and carefully. The causes which lead to drug-dependence are manifold. The individuals concerned usually are vulnerable, socially inadequate personalities, who try to escape from something, to realize a dream, or just reject authority which seems to them oppressive.

Other causes are found in the socio-cultural environment, for example, the glorification of addiction or the need of youngsters who come from the provinces in search of work, having no money or opportunity to get accommodation, and are introduced to night-clubs where they have to keep awake all night. Chance, curiosity and exploitation by drug-pedlars play further parts. Like the causes, so the complications may arise in various fields—psychological, physical, economic, social, and legal—and the problem to be faced in treatment is not only that of withdrawal of the drug, but also that of rehabilitation, so that the victim should be able to return to society as a useful citizen who is capable of earning a living without relapse.

Alcohol, in spite of the wording used in the Road Traffic Act, which refers to 'the influence of drink or drugs' is itself a drug, the still most commonly used one, and in the present social pattern in our country, the one that leads more often than any other to driving offences and to crime. The link between drinking and crime assumes ever-increasing dimensions according to Gibbens, not so much because alcohol is the principal cause of crime, but rather because 'excessive drinking with all its attendant complications of economic difficulties and marital discord, is one of the major causes of failure to recover from early delinquency'. Most alcoholics develop psychological dependence only but a minority become real addicts with the consequent danger of convulsions and *delirium tremens* on withdrawal. One cause which may lead to the habit of heavy drinking, but is not usually found in other drugs, is economic prosperity. Whether the 'alcoholic personality' is the cause or the result of alcoholism, is still an open question.

The fact which gives rise to the deepest concern is the rapid spread of addiction, particularly in the younger age-groups. For heroin, according to the Home Office index of known addicts, the number amongst the under twenties has grown from nil in 1959 to three in 1962 to forty in 1964 and to one hundred and thirty-four in 1965 (the last figure I could find). It seems that the ever increasing speed which we observe these days in every sphere of life applies also to drug-addiction, and now it often takes but two to three years to become addicted to drugs and in some cases only a few weeks. While it used to take twenty-five years to become an alcoholic, now the young alcoholic addicted over a period of about five years is seen in hospital.

If we consider the physical, psychological and moral effects of long-term addiction to alcohol or drugs, it becomes clear that a periodic medical examination of such chronic addicts is imperative to ascertain whether they are still physically and mentally fit to drive. At a Symposium in Bonn in 1955 it was reported from one district that among forty-one drug addicts, five were drivers and each one had been involved in accidents; one of them, a doctor, had had as many as four in four months. In contrast to this the analysis of 2,672 records of drivers convicted for illegal use of drugs showed that they had no more accidents than those in a comparable group, though they had a high rate of violation of the law. These figures are not explained as the effect of the drugs to which tolerance quickly develops, but rather as a reflection of the social rebellion that drives those people to the use of drugs. It was also thought that people who take drugs do not feel like driving during the brief euphoric phase that follows, and thus avoid accidents under their influence, but the report does not state the nature of the drugs taken by the drivers nor whether they had been taken over a long time, and this deprives the observations of much of their value.

The use of drugs on isolated occasions is, of course, a very different matter. It has already been mentioned that the driving ability of a very excitable person might actually be improved by the occasional use of a tranquilliser. Similarly, the occasional dose of some amphetamine might help a driver to overcome acute tiredness. Hallucinogens, however, even comparatively mild ones such as marijuana, would be likely to change normal emotions to the extent of making people oblivious of, or indifferent to, their surroundings and therefore, even under the influence of nothing more than 'reefers', there must be a greatly increased risk to driving.

6. THE DRINKING DRIVER

Acute alcohol intoxication is a special problem of very wide social implications and has very likely produced more research, discussions and suggestions than any other single element in the endeavour to reduce accidents, though as Leeming rightly points out (13.3, p. 179) we do not know to what extent the factor of drink contributes overall to the number or severity of road accidents. This problem is of great concern to the doctor who acts as police surgeon, and is called upon to certify whether a driver is under the influence of drink or drugs to an extent that makes him unfit to have proper control of a motor vehicle, according to the Road Traffic Act, 1962, 'unfit' being defined as meaning that his ability to drive properly is for the time being impaired.

The wording of the law is somewhat vague. 'His' ability to drive may be taken as a clear reference to the driver's normal ability. The words '... to drive properly ...', on the other hand, suggest some reference to the average normal rate rather than the individual driver's rate, which might be considerably higher than the average. In practice, the driver's normal driving ability can hardly ever be assessed, and the examining doctor will try to establish impairment against an average normal. As illustration, a case might be quoted which involved a Royal Naval physical-training instructor. The subsequently found extremely high urine alcohol content of 362mg% corresponding to 271mg% in the blood implied that his driving ability at the time was certainly impaired, but during the examination his behaviour was good in every respect. In a man who has good powers of concentration and co-ordination, which a physical-training instructor in the Royal Navy must necessarily possess, it is not surprising that moderate impairment would not be obvious to an examiner who did not know him. Under the law as it stood then he was, of course, not charged, but under the new Road Safety Act cases like this will be liable to penalty.

As was said before, the singling out of drink from drugs is a rather arbitrary procedure, because alcohol is a drug. Moreover, the problem might well be a mixed one, anyway in some countries. A study of Danish road traffic cases revealed that the percentage of drug-consumers was considerably higher for the drinker than for the control group in the following three sets of drugs: analgesics, antipyretics, anti-rheumatics; hypnotics, especially barbiturates; and tranquillizers. The law has evidently made some distinction because driving 'under the influence of drink' is a frequent problem and one which imposes a particular responsibility on the driver; he will hardly be able to claim the mitigating circumstances which, in the case of drugs used for therapeutic purposes—and this in our country is still the vast majority of drug cases—might apply. The reaction in cases in which alcohol as well as a drug or various drugs are taken is often difficult to analyse because the effects might, according to circumstances, be additive, potentiating or antagonistic. Combining phenobarbitone with drink produces the desired intoxication more quickly and more cheaply than drink alone, but the full details of their interreaction are not quite understood.

The problem that first and foremost faces the police surgeon is to establish whether the suspected driver is, in fact, 'unfit to drive', and if so he must exclude any other conditions which might be responsible for it. There might be some chronic ailment simulating drunkenness, like an old-standing ear infection that leads to a swaying stance and gait, or there may be an acute general (usually infective) illness. After an accident the principal diagnosis to be considered is that of concussion and, accident apart, hypoglycaemic coma and carbon monoxide (coal gas) poisoning are two conditions which in some cases might clinically be indistinguishable from alcohol intoxication. A peculiar difficulty which faces the police surgeon is the fact that there is no definite single criterion which allows him to make the diagnosis of alcohol intoxication. He has to rely on various single findings which add up to the conclusive evidence. He may have to defend his opinion in Court against the opposing solicitor or counsel who will try to pick the evidence to pieces by going over it all, point for point, and suggesting that there may be other reasons for this or that finding. To remain calm, even if he feels provoked, is one of the main assets of the medical witness. In fairness he should, however, not only tell the Court his findings, but also the precise limits of the conclusions he can reach—and this appertains not only to the drinking driver but to all police cases.

Counsel often appears surprised if a doctor comes to the conclusion 'unfit through drink ...' in spite of the co-ordination tests being performed satisfactorily, but it must be remembered that judgement is affected before co-ordination and therefore observation of the accused's behaviour in between the tests, and taking note of what he says, may be decisive factors in coming to the diagnosis. In a recent case, for example, the accused was asked:

'When did you last eat?' and he replied: 'At tea-time.' 'Had you a
drink with your meal?' 'I never drink with my meals.' 'Had you had
a drink since?' 'I never drink after meals.' 'Do you feel sick at all?'
'I feel sick all the time.' As the accused did not look as if this was
the case, the supplementary question was put: 'Tonight?' 'No,
tomorrow night' was the serious reply. This reply alone would have
sufficed for certification, but there was also a horizontal
'nystagmus' (an oscillating movement of the eyes on looking
sideways which is due to an imbalance of the eye muscles that
prevents steady focusing). This nystagmus was equal to both sides,
the pupils wide with sluggish reaction to light, features which are
not only very suggestive of alcohol intoxication but also present a
danger in themselves as they make a driver abnormally sensitive to
glare. The accused was, therefore, duly certified as unfit and
actually pleaded guilty. Incidentally, speaking of eyesight being
affected by alcohol, research carried out by the Birmingham
Ophthalmic Information Council suggests that visual powers are,
under the influence of drink, 'seriously impaired' in other respects
as well, and a driver in this condition is therefore not only slower
to react to danger when he sees it but he is, it seems, less likely to
see it clearly when it arises.

It is a well-known technique of opposing Counsel to try to
make it appear that the doctor's opinion in drinking-driver cases
is nothing more than guesswork. This, of course, is not so. The
diagnosis of alcohol intoxication is well founded on signs and
symptoms, and interpreted from experience. If it is classed as
'guesswork' all medical diagnosis must be classed as such.
However, the idea of guesswork appears to have infected even the
Minister of Transport, because in moving the second reading of
the new Road Safety Bill, Mrs Barbara Castle was reported as
saying: 'By this means we shall be taking the guesswork out of the
law on drink and driving.' Seen from the legal angle this is so, for
anybody with a blood-alcohol content of more than 80 mg% will
be committing the relevant offence. Medically speaking, the new
law is more of guesswork than the old, for it has never been
claimed that with 80mg% of alcohol in the blood every driver is
unfit in the accepted sense. It is only with regard to values of
150mg% or more that the Special Committee, set up by the
British Medical Association to investigate these problems, stated

that it could not conceive of any circumstances in which it could be considered safe for a person to drive a vehicle on the public roads.

7. MEDICAL OBSERVATIONS ON THE DRINKING-DRIVER LAW

Of course it can be claimed, and it has been claimed, in justification of the new Road Safety Act, that the statutory limit here is as fair as the statutory speed limit on the roads, but this is not a fully valid parallel. If the speed limit is slightly overstepped, a police officer may well, and often does, after having considered the extent of 'speeding' and all other circumstances, let the driver off with a warning. This is not likely to happen once a breath test has indicated that the statutory limit of drink has been exceeded. Moreover, every driver is able to check the car speed continuously, which cannot be done with the blood-alcohol level. Self-screening with breath-testing tubes before getting behind the wheel is of little use, as in a rising curve the reading may well be below the legal maximum level at the time of testing, but go beyond the legal maximum a little later while driving. With the conflicting reports on the relationship of blood levels to drink according to circumstances, the driver may be in honest error, and thus be caught unawares. It would, therefore, be desirable to impress on the public that the only 'safe' level of drink (and even that only for those who are used to it) is less than the amount corresponding to 80mg%—for no more can be absorbed into the blood than has been imbibed. In most circumstances this precaution will actually result in a blood content well below the danger level, but there are, of course, the odd circumstances when a quick drink on an empty stomach may lead to practically 100% absorption.

On balance, as long as the present basis of legislation concerned with the motorist is accepted, (*vide* Leeming's relevant chapters) the new Road Safety Act is probably the best and fairest means of dealing with the problem of the drinking driver. Though the actual proportion of drink's contribution to road accidents is still being debated, it is widely suggested that it might be sizeable; it must of course be remembered that while many drivers with fairly high alcohol levels in the blood may drive quite well under normal circumstances, and therefore are not ordinarily stopped by the police, they may not be able to cope with the unexpected situations, as their power of judgement will be impaired.

A curious feature of the Road Safety Act is the provision for a roadside breath test. In its original form the Bill provided for random tests on drivers, in the belief that their threat would be an effective deterrent to those who had drunk a fair amount but felt that they could trust themselves still to drive well enough not to be in danger of being stopped for erratic driving. When, because of public opposition, the random tests were dropped, the roadside breath tests were retained although they had lost their principal value; still as Fitzgerald says (12.2(ii), p. 172) there is in practice still some element of randomness in the powers given to the police.

It is widely acknowledged that even the Breathalyser and similar apparatus, like the one designed by Kitagawa and Wright, have not yet achieved sufficient accuracy, and anyway are too delicate and expensive to handle for use in police stations. The alternative of transporting breath samples in special bags would, on the other hand, likely lead to the loss of a fair number of samples due to air leakage. The Alcotest tubes to be used for the screening tests at the roadside are considerably less accurate, and it also takes some time after drinking—reports say anything between fifteen and forty-five minutes—to achieve a balance between the air in the lungs and in the mouth cavity. Any vomiting or belching, particularly if with it there is some regurgitation of stomach contents, may even later again upset the balance. Breath samples taken soon after the end of drinking would, therefore, show a disproportionately high level. The situation now will be this: if the police find the screening test high, they will take the suspected driver to the police station and call the police surgeon to take blood for transmission to the laboratory. If the screening test shows a level not exceeding the statutory figure of 80mg% of alcohol, the procedure should be very much the same, for if the driver has been stopped because his driving behaviour was suspect, the cause for this should still have to be investigated to find out whether it was sickness, influence of drugs, or whether the breath test failed for some peculiar reason. Consequently a second breath sample after arrest seems a superfluous procedure, wasting time and money: a blood or urine sample should be taken in every such case.

There is furthermore the possibility that a person who is unused to drink—for example the sad but well-known case where, at a works' party, 'friends' doctor the one drink the driver thinks he can safely take—or a particularly susceptible individual may be unfit to drive after a much smaller amount of drink. It may in future be even more difficult than hitherto to establish such a fact beyond reasonable doubt to the satisfaction of a jury, but in any case it seems that the attendance of a doctor at the police station remains as necessary as before, and the roadside screening test does not alter the situation. This is particularly important in view of Mr Taverne—who in a Parliamentary debate spoke on behalf of the Home Office—having been quoted in *Hansard* as saying that 'in almost all cases prosecution will be brought under the new offence provisions'. It is also important for the reason that if drivers are tested after a road accident, and one shows more alcohol than another, there may well be a presumption of guilt against him which might be unjustified, and could be disproved by clinical examination of both drivers. In these cases it would therefore be essential to have all parties concerned clinically examined, and, if needs be, brought before the court for apportionment of responsibility.

The action of small quantities of alcohol in the blood is another still open question. It has, of course, often been claimed that driving is thereby improved, but most earlier studies contradict this claim, and it was thought that the drivers only felt that their driving was improved, while actually, though a driver might still drive well, he would feel capable of better things and might therefore take risks which in some cases would lead to dangerous situations. However, the more recent reports by Borkenstein in his 'Grand Rapids' trials, and by Birrell on the experience of the Victorian Police Force over several years, indicate that the old claim might be true after all, as they found that drivers with small quantities of alcohol in the blood-stream had statistically a lower accident rate than their sober counterparts. This, however, applied only to quantities below 30mg% or perhaps 40mg%, and it is generally agreed that above 50mg% everyone's driving is impaired to some degree, that at higher levels the difference in tolerance between a seasoned drinker and a social drinker is disappearing, and that at 150mg% nobody would drive under any circumstances as the liability to accidents increases with increasing blood alcohol levels at a rate approximating to geometrical proportion.

8. THE VALUE OF CHEMICAL TESTS

The chemical tests used to determine the alcohol content in a driver's body are done either in the blood or the urine, and in the latter case the findings were until now translated into blood alcohol values according to a recognized formula: if urine was used for the test, then two subsequent samples were collected about one-half to one hour apart.

The 1967 Road Safety Act provides that the first specimen of urine shall now be disregarded by the court, and as a matter of fact it is not to be sent to the laboratory but disposed of, as in some cases it will be less reliable than the second sample. The alcohol value on the usual reckoning would be too low in comparison with the blood-alcohol content if urine had been in the bladder from the time before drinking began, similarly it would be too high if the urine had been in the bladder for so long that the blood alcohol had time to drop below the critical level. A report on the examination of both specimens would, however, have given an indication in this respect, and also have provided important clues in relation to the clinical findings, which are usually much less in a falling than in a rising curve, because behaviour returns to normal much more quickly than the blood-alcohol level does. It is to be regretted that no clinical examination is now demanded, but it is to be hoped that any doctor who is called upon to take a blood sample will also do at least a cursory examination if only to make sure that the accused is not ill and that it is safe to take the blood. Although the Road Safety Act has fixed a figure of 107mg% in the urine to be accepted as equivalent to 80mg% in the blood, and the courts, therefore, will for the present pronounce judgement accordingly, clinical observations would be of great value for the future evaluation of the Act.

There remains the question of the accuracy and margin of error in the method of analysis. Reports from Sweden, the country with probably the largest experience in this field, indicate that there a margin of 15mg% (that is three times the standard deviation of the method used there) is allowed for, and this is taken care of by the laboratory. The method now used in the Forensic Science Laboratories is that of gas chromatography which is reported to have a standard deviation below 2mg% (nearer 1 than 2) and 6mg% error will be allowed for by those laboratories, so the test will be reported as not less than 80mg% only if the mean value of the several tests is actually 86mg%. The most accurate results are in theory to be obtained from blood in the capillaries which are the finest blood vessels in the body, finer even than a hair, in which the oxygen supply to all organs takes place. This is the figure that really matters, and except in the later stages of absorption the alcohol content in these capillaries (and with it in the brain) will be higher than in the venous blood, but the venous blood will show higher values in the later stages. It has therefore been suggested that blood should be taken by a prick from the finger or an ear lobe, and actually in the attempt to popularize the Act the public were led to believe that no more than such a prick would be needed. Unfortunately it turned out that nine drops of blood are required, two samples of three drops for the laboratory, and one sample of three drops for the accused, and it is very often not possible to collect this amount from a skin-prick. In manual workers with thick or hard skin on their fingers, the Medipoint blood lancet which comes with the collecting kit and which has a point of unalterable standard length might draw no blood at all. The taking of venous blood at the police station, on the other hand, has the great disadvantage that under conditions of not very good light, and in surroundings far from sterile, it may well involve a risk of infection with resulting legal action against the doctor who, under present legislation, is not indemnified. Even a relatively unimportant leaking of the blood from the vein underneath or into the skin, though it might be unavoidable, might lead to such an action, particularly in a person under the influence of drink, who is unable, or only half willing, to co-operate. The police surgeon will therefore have to use his judgement as to how blood should be taken in each case, and in recognition of this the Home Office has arranged for syringes to be available at the police station as well as the Medipoint lancet. (See also p. 156.)

The cleansing of the skin from wherever the blood is drawn, must of course, not be done with alcohol, and Physohex or Hibitane are ideal disinfectants for the purpose.

It is open to doubt, and only time will tell, if it is wise to judge cases on the results of chemical tests alone. There are already reports of a pill, produced and marketed in Austria, which reduces the alcohol found by testing the blood by about 45% compared with the value to be expected from the drink consumed. Inquiries with the police laboratory in Vienna, for which I am indebted to Dr Walls, the Director of the Metropolitan Police Forensic Science Laboratory, have confirmed the existence of such a pill, but its exact nature and action are still obscure. It is claimed to act by accelerating the excretion of alcohol by promoting transference through the cell membranes. If this claim is correct, or if absorption of alcohol into the blood should be interfered with, the use of such a pill would be unobjectionable, as it is not the amount of alcohol consumed which matters, but the amount present in the blood, and therefore affecting the brain. If, on the other hand, it should be found that this or any other substance which might be discovered and marketed, interfered with the test or tests used for the blood-alcohol determination, thus showing amounts lower than those actually present, the whole law based on chemical results would be defeated. This position has to be watched, for, as Sir Clive Bossom said in a discussion in the House: 'There are people who will try to find ways and means of getting round the law.' There always will be.

9. CONCLUSIONS

Summing up all the facts discussed, the question arises what conclusions can be reached. The aim, of course, is to reduce the terrible number of road accidents and their consequences, and in this road engineers, lighting engineers, car designers, the makers of tyres, brakes, safety glass, and of all the other things that contribute to road safety, co-oate. The peravowed intention of the law-makers is the same, but whether they go about it in the right way is a vexed question: maybe too much emphasis is laid on the law as a deterrent—which here, as in other fields, seems to fail.

Lord Devlin, in an address to the Annual General Meeting of the

Magistrates' Association in October 1960, suggested that the terms 'careless driving' and 'dangerous driving' (commonly interpreted as bad and very bad driving) should be dropped, and instead the distinction made between bad driving and wicked driving. The same idea in modified form was taken up in a memorandum drawn up by the Law Society on 'Motoring Offences' in June 1965; this suggests that cases of bad driving should be dealt with by the magistrates without any option of trial by jury, the wicked driver would go before the Criminal Court for trial by jury. Lord Devlin supports his proposal with the argument that juries do not always see the need for discipline and, therefore, are inclined to be over-sympathetic to the careless driver, while they are an excellent body to administer the moral law, unwilling as they are to tolerate any crime which is blatantly sinful or disgraceful. If this suggestion were implemented, the driver who knowingly takes risks would obviously be dealt with by jury, and so would anyone driving under the influence of drink or drugs above the safe limit. As it is a matter within the knowledge of only the accused whether he was aware of the danger of any illness or of drugs he was taking, the Criminal Court would also try any driver who is involved in an accident due to illness, take the evidence necessary to assess his guilt, and find accordingly.

Whether automatic disqualification, even on first conviction, is the best available punishment is another vexed question, and a suggestion in the Law Society's memorandum that suspended disqualification might be introduced as a new penalty seems to have much to recommend itself. However, all the doctor can contribute to this problem is the observation that first offenders who 'get off' in Court only very rarely appear a second time for the same offence, and those who are recurrently charged for driving while under the influence of drink must be suspected of being 'problem drinkers'. This rather vague term which has recently been used in the literature is obviously meant as a polite phrase to cover the initial stages of chronic alcoholism, the phase when drinking causes more than passing problems for them, whether they be marital, social, or employment difficulties, or conflicts with the law; many of them will in time go on to the later stages of alcoholism. There seems little doubt that the same pattern will be found with the use of other drugs of addiction and here, as we said before, disqualification seems to be the only answer for the protection of the public because no means the law can provide are likely to serve the rehabilitation of those drivers.

Many attempts have been made in many countries to solve the problem of road accident prevention. A memorandum issued by the British Medical Association in March 1954 contains many valuable suggestions, and so does the previously mentioned guide drawn up by a consultant group of the World Health Organization in 1956, and one by the American Medical Association in 1959. There is also a useful paper from Germany by Borgmann, and more recent ones from Pennsylvania, New York, and Sweden. Many more reports are summarized in the proceedings of the Third International Conference on 'Alcohol and Road Traffic' in September 1962. Taking account of all the papers I could find, and the lessons drawn from them, I came to the conclusion that, while, of course, research to correlate the relationship of physical and mental disabilities with road accidents must go on, the following suggestions could, from a medical point of view, be made now.

The Swedish procedure, which requires a medical examination before any driving licence can be issued, is obviously ideal but probably not essential and in any case not, at present, practicable in this country: even selective examination might provide practical difficulties, but it appears imperative to have it introduced, even if in stages. The medical examination, now only demanded for public service vehicle drivers, should certainly be extended to all drivers of heavy vehicles, and further to all professional drivers, for those who spend their working life driving are exposed to greater risks on the road than those who only occasionally drive. Also, the professional driver, who has to work to a timetable and cannot usually take a rest in the middle of doing a job, is under much heavier strain than the private motorist, who can lighten his burden whenever he feels the need. Different standards of fitness to drive should, therefore, exist for those two different classes of road-users, and it might be as well at least to encourage, if not compel, all of the first group to have a basic knowledge of First Aid, and to carry the essential equipment.

As Fitzgerald mentions (12.3, p. 172) there are two schools of thought on which our legislation has been based, the first that the motor vehicle is to be restricted, and in this case the issue of a driving licence would be considered a privilege. The second holds that the right to drive is a natural liberty, in which case the holding of a licence is a fundamental right. The first school would hold, and the second might agree, that the medical conditions could be of sufficient importance to warrant medical examination. If so, this should be carried out by specially appointed doctors, whether singly or acting as panels seems debatable; for the family doctor it is a thankless task. The holding of a driving licence would, in this case, be made dependent on a declaration which gives consent for the examining doctors to request at any time information from the driver's personal doctor, because many disabilities may remain undetected on routine examination or may not be properly assessed without the medical history and his own doctor's opinion being available. There would also have to be a clause of consent for the provision of blood—or urine—samples, which would overcome any objection that the Road Safety Act 1967 might force an accused to provide self-incriminating evidence; to distinguish between verbal evidence and chemical evidence seems to be a very artificial differentiation.

Under the circumstances all drivers under twenty-one (or even twenty-five) should be medically examined, and in contrast to Sweden, where a licence issued to healthy persons is valid for their lifetime, all drivers should be re-examined at the age of about seventy. In between these ages an examination should be carried out on drivers whenever there is reason to suspect any physical or mental disability, on all drivers who are found driving under the influence of drink or drugs, on all who had an accident under circumstances which might suggest that there is a permanent impairment of their driving ability, and on all who had more than one major accident within three years. In every such case the driving licence should be suspended pending medical examination. The examining doctors should have the right to refer the applicant to a consultant, for special laboratory tests, or—when they think that this might provide the answer—to a driving test. On the other hand, any applicant who is dissatisfied with the medical examiner's decision should have the right of appeal to a panel of consultants, but he should not be entitled to have the issue of a driving licence made dependent on a driving test, except where the doctors agree that this would give the answer. Periodic examination should be provided for, not according to any rigid scheme but as each case requires, so that the licences could be issued for temporary periods of variable length, according to medical advice.

Whether the cost of all this can be justified, or whether, as Leeming suggests, accidents would be reduced to a greater degree if the money were to be spent on road improvements is not for a doctor to say. Certainly it will have to be taken into account that there will always be a proportion of cases in which the first incident of manifest disability seems to come 'out of the blue', and every scheme of medical examination will therefore have but limited scope for reducing the number of road accidents, even of those in which medical conditions play a part. However, any reduction in the number of accidents is a vital matter to the nation, therefore, any contribution, however small, is of major importance. But care must be taken not to over-emphasize any one group of factors, and consequently reduce research into, or measures against, others that may be even more important.

Adderdum If the collection of blood for an alcohol test is done by a skinprick from ear or finger it is likely that it will not run freely, so that squeezing is necessary to obtain the required amount. In that case, the results are not likely to be as accurate as in theory they should be. The reason may be two-fold. In consequence of the squeezing, extra tissue fluid will get into the sample and this will contain a higher proportion of alcohol than the whole blood, as blood plasma contains up to 50% more alcohol than blood corpuscles. If, on the other hand, because of the scanty blood flow, collection is slow, there will be time for evaporation to take place from the warm surface of the finger, and this will produce a lower reading of blood-alcohol, particularly in the second and third samples. The consequent large drop of alcohol content compared with the first sample may make the result of the analysis unusable.

12

ROAD TRAFFIC LAW AS THE LAWYER SEES IT

By PROFESSOR P. J. FITZGERALD, M.A., Barrister-at-Law

'Bad laws are the worst sort of tyranny.' *Burke*

TODAY'S average criminal, it is said, is not a thug or a thief, but a driver. In 1967, the 'criminal on the road' was the subject of 64% of all cases heard in the criminal courts. He was the victim of 88% of all convictions before the magistrates, and he committed about a million and a half offences and alleged offences. Unlike the thief, who comes a poor second—only 9% of criminal cases concerned larceny—and who must rest content with the ordinary criminal law, the traffic offender has a whole chapter of law to himself. To evaluate this law—to ask, for example, whether speed limits promote safety or not—is a matter for the expert in the field, the traffic engineer. On such questions, lawyers can indeed speak, but their voices are those of laymen. What lawyers *qua* lawyers can discuss, about this, as about any, branch of law, is the question of formal expression, the requirements of justice and the problem of enforcement. As a lawyer, one asks three questions about our traffic law. Is it clear? Is it fair? And is it effective? Our traffic law, I shall contend, is none of these.

1. CLARITY AND THE TRAFFIC LAW

To be clear, laws must be simple. They must not suffer from what Bentham termed over-bulkiness! Yet the *Encyclopædia of Road Traffic Law* already runs into nearly two thousand pages. There are twenty-seven relevant statutes already in existence, and more are on the way. Road Traffic Rules and Orders total no less than two hundred and twenty-seven, and it has been calculated that there are about a thousand regulations which a driver can infringe. Enough to daunt Bentham himself, let alone the ordinary driver, unskilled in law; and all the more surprising when, as Professor R. M. Jackson has remarked, there is really little area of doubt about the duties and obligations of drivers. Good law should be clear, and clarity cannot be expected from this sort of multiplicity of regulations.

A second enemy to clarity is ambiguity. In law, a measure of ambiguity is inevitable. It arises from the nature of language itself. All rules, including legal rules, are concerned with general kinds of acts and things, and must be couched in sentences employing general words. Now all such words suffer from what philosophers call 'open texture'. They apply clearly enough to a central cluster of acts or things, but not so clearly to cases on the borderline. 'Nighttime' applies without doubt to midnight and the small hours, but what about dusk and dawn? To overcome this problem, the law relating to burglary (which can only be committed at night) has arbitrarily defined night-time to extend from 9 p.m. to 6 a.m. But it is not every borderline case that can be foreseen or legislated against, so that we should not cavil at the draughtsman's failure to define each word in the statutes with unerring precision. Still, we might have expected that the most important word of all, and the one central to all road traffic offences, would be defined with some care or exactness. I refer to 'driving'. Though partially defined in S257(1) of the 1960 Act, so as to cover both the steersman and another where both are engaged in driving a vehicle, this word is nowhere comprehensively defined. Of course we know what ordinarily counts as driving: the paradigm case is where one and the same person steers and is responsible for the vehicle's propulsion by its engine. But what of the borderline case where a man steers a car downhill when its engine is out of action? What about the case where a person steers a towed vehicle? These and similar problems have been left to the courts, whose decisions have not been conspicuous for consistency. To steer an engineless car downhill has been held to be driving. To steer one on tow not. But to steer one which was pushed by a man behind, was deemed to be driving. Yet to steer one pushed from behind by another vehicle, was held not to be driving. As a lawyer one might have hoped, and as a driver one might well demand, to be spared this sort of ambiguity and confusion, however difficult precision may be to achieve.

Still less defensible is that sort of ambiguity which arises, not from the inherent nature of language, but from lack of clarity in syntactical arrangement. A glance at the annual returns for motoring offences confirms that one of the commonest of all offences is that of careless driving. Section 3(1) of the 1960 Act defines this as driving 'without due care and attention, or without reasonable consideration for other persons using the road'. A harmless enough phrase to all appearances, but what does it really mean? Am I guilty of driving without due care and attention only if I drive *both* without due care *and* without attention? Of course, if I drive without attention, I automatically drive without due care, but I could pay lots of attention and still drive without due care; and, on the above interpretation, I would go scot-free because my driving does not lack both elements. Or does it mean merely that I can commit the offence *either* by driving without due care *or* by driving without attention? On this interpretation, paying attention, but not taking care, would not escape the law. Common sense of course suggests that the 'and' is disjunctive, and that lack of due care, and lack of attention, is each by itself sufficient to constitute the offence. But common sense is no infallible guide, because the law is not always common-sensical. So, pedantic as the problem may seem, this is the sort of stuff that law-cases are made of, and the fact that this particular problem has not so far troubled the courts, may well be because no one has sought to raise it, and because it is only comparatively recently that syntactic ambiguity has started to interest the lawyer.

But the greatest foe to clarity is plain obscurity. This can arise from bad draughtsmanship, and the use of gobbledy-gook, a type of defect from which road traffic law is, on the whole, mercifully free. It can arise where the law speaks with different voices on the same subject, contradicting in one section what it has said in another; and, again, road traffic law itself seems comparatively free from this, though at the lower level of implementation, it is not uncommon for the driver to find himself confronted with contradictory orders. I have seen, for instance, in one city street, two notices restricting parking along the same stretch of road, one of which stated that parking was permitted for one hour in any two hours, while the other stated that parking was permitted for thirty minutes in any hour. (See also 8.2, p. 93.) Most disquieting, however, is the obscurity that arises from interpretive judicial decisions shedding darkness rather than light. This is what happened with the offence of dangerous driving.

'Driving in a manner which is dangerous to the public,' as ordinarily understood, would comprise the case of driving in a way that visibly endangers (or could endanger) other members of the public: there must be something dangerous about the very manner in which the vehicle is driven. The courts, however, have extended the phrase to cover what Professor Glanville Williams has called 'invisible' cases of dangerous driving, for example, the driving of a car which is in an unroadworthy condition, and the driving of a car by a driver not fit to drive, however careful the actual manner of the driving. One may not object overmuch to this extension, because, although the driver may be driving safely and carefully in both cases, it is nevertheless dangerous to drive when the driver or his vehicle is not in a fit condition. What is confusing, though, and therefore objectionable, is what the courts have said with regard to negligence and the offence of dangerous driving.

A common-sense view, and one in line with the scheme of the statute, and the history of the law on the subject, is that there are four different degrees of negligence. The highest degree is that necessary for manslaughter. Dangerous driving requires less negligence than manslaughter, but more than careless driving, and careless driving needs more negligence than suffices to render the driver liable in civil law. But the courts have suggested that dangerous driving is an absolute offence, and have said that if the manner of driving is dangerous, it matters not whether the defendant was deliberately reckless, careless, momentarily inattentive or even doing his incompetent best. This not only obliterates the distinction between dangerous and careless driving; it means that you can be guilty of the more serious offence with a lesser degree of fault than that required for the minor offence.

And road traffic law teems with such problems. One never knows, for instance, until a court pronounces, whether an offence is absolute or not, and if it is, exactly what this means. These and similar problems are of course matters of detail fit for meticulous legal analysis, a thorough examination being outside the scope of this chapter.

Enough has been said, I hope, to indicate not only the sort of contribution lawyers can make by concentrating on the form rather than the substance of the law, but also the kinds of defects in road traffic law waiting to be remedied. Law that is unclear is objectionable on many grounds. It confuses the courts, adds to their work and wastes the time of all who have to unravel it. It leaves the citizen uncertain of his duties and obligations, and exposed to the possibility of penal sanctions for unwitting violations—a situation as ridiculous as it is unfair.

2. FAIRNESS AND THE TRAFFIC LAW

Unfairness, however, can also arise on other grounds. It is not enough merely that the law be known and understood. Justice demands that the law—and particularly the criminal law—refrains from penalizing conduct 'unmeet for punishment', and discriminating against any particular section of the community. Road traffic law offends against both these principles. It seeks to punish behaviour to which attaches little, if any, moral blame; and it is discriminatory, no less by reason of the inescapably random nature of its enforcement than by its denial to the driver of equal treatment by the law. I shall examine briefly both of these propositions.

(a) TRAFFIC OFFENCES UNFIT FOR PUNISHMENT

Morally speaking, we should not penalize acts unless they are morally wrong. Now, traffic offences consist almost entirely of three kinds, all of which may be argued to be lacking in immorality. These are (i) offences of negligence, (ii) technical offences such as 'speeding', and (iii) offences of strict liability. To the man in the street, these are hardly crimes at all. This can be seen from the fact that no matter how many his driving convictions, the traffic offender is never popularly termed a criminal. It can be seen from the prevalence of the view that the motorist is unjustly persecuted by the police, and hounded by the law, no less than from the existence of the contrary view that the authorities treat him all too leniently, and decline to regard him as a real criminal. And, indeed, he does appear to receive different treatment. One in every five offences, or alleged offences, on the road, is dealt with by written warning in lieu of prosecution; special days are reserved in some courts for traffic offences; traffic offences are distinguished from other offences when the court comes to the accused's record for previous convictions; and the average fine for the traffic offence is low—under £6 was the average fine for all offences in 1967.

Now one feature distinguishing traffic offences from ordinary crimes is the number of people that commit them. Murder, rape and stealing are things which the average person does not do. Careless driving and 'speeding', on the other hand, are offences which anyone and everyone at some time may commit. Ordinary crimes, then, are deviations from the norm, while traffic crimes appear to be themselves the norm. Indeed it is notorious the extent to which certain traffic regulations are disregarded. It is almost conventional to drive about ten miles an hour faster than the speed limit, and how many drivers obey a 'no parking' sign if they know they will not be caught? Of course, if regulations are made for the common good, their infringement is anti-social, and there is a view that the purpose of the criminal law ought to be solely the prevention or reduction of anti-social behaviour. On the other hand, the enforcement of such an aim against a very widespread section of the population runs into practical difficulties. Cost alone will allow nothing more than a random enforcement, while popular feelings will hardly countenance penalties large enough to be wholly deterrent, for example, to parking offences.

In short, the traffic offender as he sees himself, and as others see him, is an ordinary respectable law-abiding citizen whose only misfortune has been to violate a traffic regulation. This view has been attacked in the now classic study by Willett,* who has tried to establish that far from being in other regards respectable, the traffic offender is likely—more likely than the non-offender—to have previous convictions for non-motoring offences. Willett's own conclusions, however, are open to criticism. In the first place, his research concentrated exclusively on serious offences, that is, causing death by dangerous driving, dangerous driving, driving under the influence of drink or drugs, failure to stop after, or to report, an accident, failure to insure against third-party risks, and driving while disqualified. No attention at all was devoted to careless driving, speeding and all the other minor violations which form the bulk of our traffic offences. If Willett's findings show that a man drives as he lives, and that a man who commits a serious driving offence is quite likely to have committed other

---

* T. C. Willett, *Criminal on the Road.* London: Tavistock Publications.

non-driving offences, might not a parallel piece of research show that a man who commits a minor traffic offence is quite unlikely to have committed *any* non-driving offence? But Willett's findings, it seems, do not bear out his own conclusions, even as regards the serious offender. Steer and Carr-Hill (*The Motoring Offender: Who is He?* 1967. Crim. LR, pp. 214–22) and Leeming (AU, 19.8.66) have shown that his conclusions would have been very different had he omitted the two offences of driving uninsured or driving while disqualified. Those in his survey convicted of these offences had a totally disproportionate record of previous non-motoring offences, which distorted the overall picture. Remove these two from the list, and the picture of the serious driving offender as otherwise respectable once more emerges.

For the thing which, above all for the man in the street, distinguishes the criminal from the traffic offender, is the same thing that differentiates ordinary crimes from driving offences, viz. that criminal acts are, and driving offences are not, according to ordinary thinking, immoral. And although it is sometimes argued that infringements of the traffic law are also infringements of the moral law, ordinary thinking is, as often, not too wide of the mark. To show this, let me consider the three types of traffic offence.

(i) *Negligence.* The two central offences in the driving law are dangerous driving and careless driving. Both are basically crimes of negligence which common sense regards as not all that immoral, and certainly not so reprehensible as deliberate wrongdoing. In this, common sense is but copying the ordinary criminal law which, manslaughter apart, has nothing to do with negligence. What the basic criminal law is concerned with are acts which deliberately violate the rights of others, and real crimes consist for the most part of intentional attacks on the person and property of others: Assault is a crime, but injury by carelessness is not; stealing is a crime, but taking through some careless mistake things that do not belong to you is not. Compared with assault, theft and so on, dangerous and careless driving appear not only less immoral, but also less 'illegal'.

For this there are several reasons. In the first place, assault, theft, and so on, result in actual harm, whereas the majority of instances of dangerous and careless driving, merely result in potential harm. Secondly, before I can be proved guilty of the average common law crime, I must be shown to have had *mens rea,* which means in most cases that I must have intended to do what I did, or to do something very like it. By contrast, the two driving offences, though they can be committed intentionally—I can deliberately drive in an extremely dangerous manner—will in most cases be unintentional, and result simply from lack of care. And an act is always more culpable when intentional than when unintentional; to do harm without meaning to is never so wrong as to do it on purpose.

Thirdly, in crimes of negligence, the defendant can, to some extent, argue that he cannot help what he has done. 'I couldn't help it' is as good a defence in law as it is in morals, and the moral philosopher's dictum that ought implies can is paralleled by the legal maxim *lex non cogit ad impossibilia*—the law does not compel the impossible. The fact that the defendant was compelled to do what he did—by overbearing force, by a blow on the head or by some sudden fit over which he has no control—would count as a defence in law, even to a charge of an offence of strict liability.

On the face of it, however, 'I didn't mean' is a far cry from 'I couldn't help it'. Yet, look at an example common enough on the roads today: A is driving behind B, and C is approaching from the other direction; A overtakes B and collides with C. Clearly, in this case A has fallen below the standard of care and prudence required on the roads. Less clear is the way in which this shortfall came about. There are numerous reasons for carelessness, and their variety is simply obscured by grouping them together under the umbrella of negligence, for the only thing in common to them all is the fact that the defendant fell short of the requisite standard of care.

In the example given it could be (1) that A saw the risk and decided to run it; (2) that he saw what was happening, but failed to see the seriousness of the risk; (3) he did not notice C, possibly through inattention; (4) his eyes played him false and he mistook C for something else; (5) he made a misjudgement, for example, he miscalculated the time, or the road space needed to overtake successfully; (6) he forgot something, for example, that his present car had a less powerful engine than the one he traded in last week; (7) his mind wandered and left him carrying on driving automatically, in the same way as royal personages have been known to continue waving to the crowds which have long been left behind; or (8) he is just a poor, incompetent driver, through congenital lack of co-ordination or through lack of experience.

In one of these alternatives, the first, the driver clearly decided to fall below the standard of care. In all the others it can be said that he did not mean to do so, and also to a greater or lesser extent I would argue that he could not help doing so. A man cannot always help his clumsiness or inexperience,* and although the law may refuse to take this into account (and perhaps in some cases rightly) nevertheless morality must have regard to his 'personal equation'. Lower down the scale come (4) and (5). Of course it is a nuisance and a trial when our senses play us false, or our calculations go wrong, but how far can we really help it? We can, and should, try to take care, look carefully and get our calculations right, but all we can do is our best. Take (3) inattention, (6) forgetting, and (7) absent-mindedness; of course we say these things ought not to happen, but even Homer nods. And what are we to make of (2), the man who simply fails to appreciate the risk? In all of these there is an element of unavoidability. Men are not infallible, but have a built-in liability to error.

In lumping all these types of conduct together, the law itself is guilty of two mistakes. First, it obscures the vital distinction between deliberate and unintentional risk-taking—something which should surely be avoided, and which could be if the law drew the sort of distinction suggested by the Law Society Memorandum of 1965 and differentiated between 'reckless driving' (a deliberate and conscious violation of the law) and 'improper use of the roads' falling short of such recklessness. Secondly, it is guilty of a misguided perfectionism that asks too much of the human machine. Might it not be better to accept the fact that to err is human, to recognize that accidents will happen and to learn to live with them? In other words, instead of seeking to punish human error, the law should look for ways of avoiding or minimizing its consequences. The lesson the learner-driver has to learn is one that the law itself seems to have forgotten, viz. that you cannot rely on the other driver not to do something foolish.

---

* There is, of course, also the possibility that the law itself has caused, or contributed to, his inexperience by suspending his licence. (J.J.L.)

By trying to treat carelessness as a crime, and by judging the driver by the objective standard of the perfect but non-existent reasonable man, the law itself is forgetting that no one on the road is guaranteed against mistakes.

(ii) *Technical offences.* Still, we do to some extent condemn carelessness and the gulf between the law and morality is not complete. The same cannot be said about all the technical offences with which road traffic laws abound—acts which are forbidden by law, but which it would be pedantic to call in every case immoral. 'Speeding', illegal parking and a host of other minor infractions are not so much 'real' crimes as quasi-crimes.

Now it may be said that the only difference between a real and a quasi-crime, is one of degree. Both are anti-social, but one is a great deal more so than the other. This being so, the law is right to reject, and common sense wrong to suggest, any basic distinctions between them.

But common sense, I shall argue, is right and is grounded on the fact that the real crime differs significantly from the quasi-crime in two respects. First, it is a breach of a rule fundamental to society, whereas a quasi-crime violates a rule lacking this fundamental quality. Murder, wounding, and assault, are infringements of social rules against violence, and these rules are basic to society in that without them society would be not merely the poorer, it would be unthinkable. Part of the very idea of a society is that of a community of individuals sharing a common life, and showing reciprocal respect for one another's rights, the most important of which is the right of personal inviolability. Accordingly, a society with no rules against violence could not exist; it would not qualify as a society at all. Agreed, the rules need not be legal ones. There could be a society without any legal prohibition of violence, but one without any rules legal or moral—where there was no acceptance at all of norms or standards forbidding violence—is inconceivable. Such rules are the necessary preconditions to the very existence of society. Small wonder that their breach should be regarded entirely differently from infringements of the speed limit or parking rules, rules which may improve society, but are in no way essential to it.

Secondly, the real crime is something committed against a specific victim. Murder, rape and assault may be offences against the Queen's peace, but the vital feature about them is that some particular person gets hurt. Speeding, driving without a licence, and so on, harms no identifiable individual.

This is not to say that all the technical rules we have are in every way unnecessary, though it may not always matter what is the exact nature of the rule. For instance, we must have some rule of the road, though morality does not lay down precisely what it should be. In England, the rule of the road is left as a matter of custom rather than law, so that while, in most cases, disregard of it will amount to at least careless driving, there may well be circumstances where its disregard entails no offence. Here, law is seen at its best, combining guidance with flexibility.

It is precisely this lack of flexibility which is the most objectionable feature of the quasi-crime. The effect of regulations creating technical offences is to supplement the ordinary rules of prudence by rules of statutory prudence. Whereas regulations prohibiting negligence enforce and underwrite the rule that you must drive safely, these other regulations supersede this flexible rule by laying down what shall count as safe. If a road carries a 30 mile/h speed limit, it is no use arguing that it is safe to drive at 35 mile/h or that public interest does not require the limit. But while this may often make it easier to establish that an offence has been committed, it runs counter to what should surely be a basic principle of traffic law, that 'no driver should be placed in jeopardy from the law for doing something that is not in itself dangerous'. Detailed regulations should support rules of common sense, not become a substitute for them, or conflict with them.

How far we should legislate prudence is debatable. Bentham has argued that rules of prudence stand least in need of the assistance of legislation, because they are only broken through defects of understanding. The idea of a Highway Code with evidentiary rather than legal effect, was surely the right approach to the problem.

(iii) *Strict liability*. If crimes of negligence and quasi-crimes are objectionable, crimes of strict liability such as failure to conform to a Halt sign are indefensible. Common law requires that before a man can be guilty he must be at fault. Strict liability allows him to be convicted and punished without any fault on his part whatsoever, or even when he is behaving prudently

(6.2, p. 94) and mistake, which is a defence to an ordinary crime, and which, if reasonable, is a defence to a crime of negligence, is no defence to a crime of strict liability. All that matters is that the defendant has done the act proscribed by law.

The arguments for and against strict liability are too well known to be rehearsed here. The traditional defences of the concept are as hackneyed as they are unsound. Of course it would be harder and trials would take more time if the prosecution had to prove that the accused was at fault. But murder convictions, too, would be easier to get if malice did not have to be established.

Admittedly, it would be hard for the prosecution to prove whether the driver saw, knew, and so on, what he should have seen or known, because only the driver himself actually has this knowledge. But then, again, only the man accused of theft or receiving really knows if he had dishonest intent or knowledge, but this does not stop prosecutors from getting convictions. Alternatively, if it were too great a burden to make the prosecution prove the driver's knowledge, and so on, then why not, instead of having absolute offences, put the burden of proof on the driver? Let him prove that he made a reasonable mistake—or else be convicted.

What common sense and morality alike object to is a practice whereby the law intervenes and penalizes a man who (*a*) was not morally to blame, and (*b*) had no chance to conform to the law's requirements, since the circumstances precluded him from knowledge that he was doing something forbidden by law. If 'speeding' is an absolute offence, then you could be guilty in law if you drove 1 m.p.h. above the limit, even though you thought you were within the limit, and had every reason to think you were. For example, your speedometer might be slightly wrong, and yet there might be nothing to put you on your guard or on inquiry—no possible reason to suspect that it was wrong: it may have even been checked quite recently.

What possible justification can there be for punishing this sort of man? He was not trying to break the law: on the contrary, he was trying to conform to it. 'It will make him more careful for the future, and make others watch out too.' This line of argument takes us back to Admiral Byng. Perhaps if we hanged the odd driver who was driving with all propriety, all the bad drivers would behave better and watch out all the more. But the price we should pay would be (*a*) that the law would fall even further into disrepute, and (*b*) that we should be doing what our ordinary morality forbids—doing exactly what Kant inveighed against—using persons as things, sacrificing some for the general good. No one in his senses is going to suggest hanging the odd motorist, but the illustration dramatizes all that is objectionable in absolute offences. And in so far as traffic offences are of this nature—dangerous driving itself has been said to be so—the law offends our ordinary notions of morality, involves lack of respect for human dignity, and gives rise to a wholly deserved disrespect for the law itself.

(*b*) DISCRIMINATION AGAINST THE DRIVER

The existence of crimes of negligence, quasi-crimes, and crimes of strict liability in our traffic law, means that the traffic law is more severe on the offending driver than is the ordinary law on the ordinary offender. If this severity is justified, by reason of the enormous harm caused by road accidents, then why is it only the driver who is singled out for special treatment? Admittedly, dangerous and careless cycling are now offences too, but have only been so since 1960. As yet there is no such offence as careless walking, though pedestrians are just as capable as motorists of causing accidents. The Law Society, in their Memorandum, recommend that improper use of the road by road-users, including pedestrians, should be an offence, and this inclusion is surely long overdue. Time surely, too, to remove another inequality and deprive the animal owner of his age-old immunity from negligence. A friend of mine recently ran into some horses which had strayed onto the main road late at night, and which he had no reason to expect and no means of avoiding. His car was a write-off and his passenger seriously injured. And the owner of the horses? Though his horses were noted for straying, his only offence was a summary one under the Highways Act, 1959, S.135, and his civil-liability was nil. For the law says that there is no duty to fence your horses in. Is it surprising that drivers often feel a persecuted class, when almost alone of all road-users, they are exposed to severe penalties, have to be licensed, have to insure against third-party risks, and have to stop and report accidents?

Or, again, what of all the accidents other than road accidents? Why are accidents in the home, with firearms and with fireworks unpunished? According to the report of the Inspectors of Explosives there were 376 serious accidents with fireworks in 1965, and the number of people treated in hospital for injuries caused by fireworks was 2,339 (T, 24.6.67) about as many as it is claimed that the new Drink-Drivers Act will save. If anything, the law should favour driving as against letting off fireworks. Driving at least fulfils a valuable social purpose; letting off fireworks contributes nothing to the community at all.

The requirements of driving licences and compulsory insurance have, of course, much to be said in their favour. Licences have been compulsory since 1903, and the common good may best be served by some form of testing or licensing. But fairness might well demand that cyclists and horse-riders, too, be debarred from using the roads without a licence. The virtue of the driving licence is first that persons unfit to drive can be refused licences, and secondly that offenders can have their licences withdrawn. But disqualification has problems too. As Leeming maintains (13.6, p. 190) lack of practice may result in deterioration in driving skill, so that the offender who is disqualified, returns to the road a worse driver than before he left it; and this hardly accords with our present-day penal thinking in general, which emphasizes the paramount importance of reformation. Secondly, there seems to be evidence that disqualification is to a great extent ignored by that section of the public on whom it is most imposed, that is, the relatively young motor-cyclist of working-class origin, and the youngster who joy-rides. If this is so, then we are faced with a formidable problem of enforcement—can we really put them all in prison, and anyway, would we want to?—and also with a problem of injustice, because disqualification would seem to be a punishment only affecting the honest driver who obeys the law. You cannot cut a man off the roads as easily as off the telephone.

The justification of the requirement of insurance is that the driver must make sure that any victim of his negligence can be adequately compensated. The driver is indulging in a hazardous activity from which he benefits and, so it is said, he must foot the bill of insuring against accidents. But no one can seriously maintain that in 1969 the driver is the only beneficiary. The whole of society benefits nationally from our road traffic communications. Should not society as a whole, then, shoulder the burden, and bear the cost of insurance?

Further features supporting the view that the law discriminates against the motorist are not hard to find. First, there are the virtually fixed penalties under the 1960 Act and the present totting-up system, which compare strangely with the ordinary criminal law, which is content to lay down merely a maximum penalty. Secondly, there is the driver's duty to stop and report accidents—a sensible enough provision, but why confined to drivers and not extended to the authors of other types of accident? Thirdly, there is one's duty, where a driver is alleged to be guilty of a traffic offence, to give information when required which may lead to the identification of the driver—again, why confine to traffic offences, and why this departure from the general rule that you have no duty to give information leading to the identification of an offender against the ordinary criminal law, whether you are asked or not? And now on top of this we have the Road Safety Act, 1967, which makes it an offence to drive with over a certain quantity of alcohol in the blood. The pros and cons of this I leave to the experts, my own view tending to agree with that of Leeming. What concerns me as a lawyer is the provision for the statute's implementation. It is now an offence to refuse to give a breath specimen if required. It is also an offence to refuse to give a blood or urine specimen when required. Apart from the criticism that once again the law is discriminating against the motorist, there are more serious objections. In the first place, the statute is now forcing a man to give evidence against himself and offending against the well-established legal principle of the right to silence— a right which, with all respect to those who argue for its abolition, we should not abandon lightly. Secondly, the statute compels a man to give specimens of his body against his will—a new departure in our law, and surely one which would qualify as subjecting him to 'cruel, inhuman or degrading treatment' as prohibited by both the Universal Declaration of Human Rights and the European Convention for the Protection of Human Rights.

Enough has been said to show that the motorist can justly

complain against discrimination. Racial discrimination is more objectionable, of course. Imagine the horror that would have been created if the Road Safety Act had prescribed random tests for coloured people only. This would have been discrimination with a vengeance, for once a Negro always a Negro. The driver is better off because no one is a driver all the time. But the fact remains that a section of the population is being discriminated against, and unless it is the policy of the law to discourage the activity altogether, it is hard to perceive its justification.

Random tests were omitted from the 1967 Act, but it is questionable what difference the omission really makes, because a policeman can require a breath test if he has reasonable cause (i) to suspect that the driver has alcohol (no amount is specified) in his body, or (ii) to suspect him of committing a traffic offence while the vehicle was in motion—and this is pretty wide, or (iii) to believe that the person involved in an accident, to whom he wishes to give the breath test, was the person driving the vehicle at the time of the accident. Room here, surely, for fairly random enforcement if the police so desired.

3. EFFECTIVENESS AND THE TRAFFIC LAW

Law that is neither clear nor fair cannot hope to be effective. And the ineffectiveness of the traffic law is shown by the increasing number of court cases, the failure to stem the tide of accidents, and the general national alarm concerning the problem of road traffic.

Now the effectiveness of any law depends on what it sets out to achieve. Here, too, I suggest is one clue to the unsatisfactoriness of this part of the law. For underlying road traffic law, it has been said, there is no clear consistent philosophy. The law has become what it is for historical reasons, resulting from a basic and continuing conflict between two diametrically opposed attitudes. One group considers the motor vehicle a lethal weapon, to be jealously restricted, if not altogether banned from the roads. The other regards the right to drive as the natural liberty of every Englishman, and looks on all regulations as unwarranted encroachments on freedom. In consequence, the law has produced an unhappy compromise in which the former view has gradually but ineluctably gained ground over the latter.

In point of fact, neither view is tenable. Motor vehicles can, of course, be used as lethal weapons, and indeed have been. But this does not mean that they are designed as such, like guns and bombs; nor does it mean that they are generally used as such. To designate them 'lethal weapons' is to dramatize the fact that they are dangerous instruments at the cost of overlooking the fact that the motoring population in general does not use them to inflict deliberate harm, any more than does the scientist who experiments with dangerous chemicals. Moreover, the benefits of motorized transport are such that none but the most hardened *laudator temporis acti* would wish to revert to a Sark-like condition of life.

On the other hand, the dangers are self-evident, no less than the many other disadvantages highlighted, for example, in the Buchanan Report. Furthermore, if any activity requires co-operation and give-and-take, it is our use of the roads. Regulations and restrictions, therefore, are not only desirable, but inevitable, not only in the interests of safety, but in order to allow motoring to be carried on at all in a highly populated community.

Now, any national system of traffic law, should surely aim primarily at two objectives: (*a*) to promote the traffic flow, and (*b*) to prevent road accidents.

Instead of promoting the traffic flow, the law appears more concerned to hinder it. Road Traffic Law consists of 'don'ts' rather than 'do's'. This, of course, is because it is part of the criminal law, which rightly consists of prohibitions rather than commandments. But the question it raises is whether traffic law is properly located within the criminal law. As it is, maximum speed limits, rather than minimum ones, are the order of the day: the driver is forbidden to do this and that, instead of being urged and encouraged to drive well, safely and considerately. How much encouragement does the English driver get to form extra lines of traffic in order to speed up the traffic flow? How much importance is paid here, as contrasted with the case in the United States, to the idea of a traffic pattern, and the notion that the main thing is not to drive idiosyncratically (albeit with 'pedantic rectitude'), but in harmony with the pattern? Typical of our whole legal approach is the way the policeman is always portrayed as imperiously halting the traffic: he is the man who, in the words of the song, can 'Stop the whole street with one wave of his hand'. Contrast the French gendarme, who is always shown as furiously calling on the traffic to keep it moving. If the law is at fault here, it is because basically our attitude, or that of those in authority, has not concerned itself sufficiently with the need to get the traffic flowing systematically. After all, the whole point about cars is that they are built to travel at a steady speed from one point to another.

Even worse, however, is the law's approach to accident prevention. The idea implicit in the traffic law, seems to be this: accidents don't just happen, they are caused; they are caused by the driver, and the law's job is to punish him accordingly. Yet, if we really want to prevent road accidents, the prime problem is not whether this or that particular driver was at fault, but how this individual accident happened. Between these two questions lies a world of difference, as Leeming has shown. Collingwood puts the point neatly in a famous passage:

> (15) 'A car skids while cornering at a certain point, turns turtle, and bursts into flames. From the car driver's point of view, the cause of the accident was cornering too fast, and the lesson is that one must drive more carefully. From the county surveyor's point of view, the cause was a defective road surface, and the lesson is that one must make skid-proof roads. From the motor manufacturer's point of view, the cause was defective design, and the lesson is that one must place the centre of gravity lower.' Collingwood, *On the So-called Idea of Causation*. Proc. Aristotelian Society, xxxviii, 85 at p. 93.

What we need, then, is not a trial to find out if the driver broke the law, but an investigation to discover exactly what happened and why. Here I would agree with Leeming (15.5, p. 205) that our present system of accusatorial criminal trial is basically inimical to scientific discovery of the causes of accidents. In the first place, its objective is the wrong one. Secondly, if the driver is convicted or acquitted, there the matter ends and the file is closed. Thirdly, the person who in most cases may best be able to tell what happened, the driver, is afraid to speak out for fear of convicting himself.

But criticism is always easier than constructive suggestion, and this chapter has no blue-print for a satisfactory alternative. The best I can offer is one or two suggestions for others to think about.

The first is this, that we should adopt the Law Society's recommendation and distinguish between cases of deliberately dangerous or reckless motoring, and all other cases. The former should be dealt with by the ordinary criminal law, just as are murder, assault, robbery, and so on. More difficult is what to do with the other cases, cases where accidents happen without any obvious reckless motoring.

Ideally, we could investigate these by some special procedure. To my mind, this should be taken right out of the criminal law. Instead, there should be a form of accident inquiry, similar to inquiries into aviation accidents. The investigating body should contain a motoring expert, a traffic engineer, and a legal assessor. There would still remain, however, the problem that, as the inquiry proceeds, the finger of guilt might begin to point at the driver or some other road-user. He might, in fact, have caused the accident, wholly or partly, by what the Law Society calls 'improper use of the road'. We could, therefore, at this stage, caution him that he might be prosecuted and issue the usual warnings about what he said being used as evidence. But this would have the effect of inhibiting his evidence from that point on, and even in some cases, from the very beginning. Alternatively, we could adopt a system whereby, even if he were guilty of improper use of the roads, no prosecution or penalty would follow. This would purchase open and frank evidence by the driver at the cost of allowing improper driving (less than reckless) to go unpunished. But, then, everything has its price. My contention is that the gain in discovery would be worth the impunity involved.

I realize that many will regard this suggestion as fantastic. Nevertheless, I maintain that there is nothing to be said for treating negligence, technical infringements and offences of strict liability as crimes. As Professor Jackson has said: 'It is hard to believe that prosecuting more and more people every year is the best way of securing a good-tempered community, that accepts and observes codes of conduct designed for everyone's safety and convenience.'

13

DOUBT AND HUNCH

'Search in and out and round about,
And you'll discover never,
A tale so free from every doubt—
All probable, possible shadow of doubt—
All possible doubt whatever.'
The Grand Inquisitor in The Gondoliers, *by W. S. Gilbert*

1. WHAT DO WE KNOW?

Those who have read the preceding chapters objectively will now realize that we know very little. It is, unlike Don Alhambra's problem in the song quoted above, a tale riddled with doubts and, above all, with the central problem hidden from us. Great claims are made to knowledge, but they are almost invariably mere hunch.

In Chapters 6 and 7 I have shown that before-and-after studies have given us some information. We can be confident that road improvements, if properly done and not cut down in the interests of 'economy', can make very substantial reductions in accidents, and, if really suitable for the conditions, can even eliminate fatalities. I have set out my own evidence for this in Tables 10, 13 and 14 (pp. 46, 57 and 68), but other evidence comes from all over the world in overwhelming volume. No reasonable person can reject it. Some of the results in Table 10 appear disappointing, but this is due to the inclusion of sites at which the work was not up to modern standards. I repeat that *I have used all the sites sent to me, and have not rejected any on grounds of unusual conditions* even when it might have seemed reasonable to do so. The table also shows that road improvements sometimes reduce fatal and serious accidents more than minor ones, and that it is comparatively rare for them to increase accidents. Only in 23 out of 256 sites—9%—has this happened, while at 166 of the sites—65%—accidents were reduced, all in section (*a*) of Table 10.

The results in section (*b*) of Table 10, of legal engineering measures, are much less successful than the civil engineering ones, and some have the reverse effect of reducing fatal and serious accidents less than minor ones. They also reduce accidents less often than the civil engineering ones, only at 36% of sites, while at 28% of sites they have increased. So far as I know, the samples used

176

for Table 10 are the first to be large enough to have made it possible to study the fatalities alone, and it is disquieting to find that in the only two speed limits—40 and 50—it has been possible to analyse both show an *increase in fatalities*. Admittedly these are not significant, but they support each other, and they are as 'conclusive' as much of the evidence which Mrs Castle claimed 'proves' that speed limits stop accidents.

The first of the many questions we must ask, of which I shall give a small selection in this chapter, is why are legal measures so relatively less successful than civil engineering ones?

2. THE VEHICLE

There has been much discussion of this aspect recently, especially in the U.S.A. and much publicity has been given to the books by Nader, and by O'Connell and Myers. Mackay has discussed it in Chapter 10, and I have little to add to that.

One matter impinges on the function of the traffic engineer, and on propaganda. The two books I have mentioned sharply criticize the American motor manufacturers for being reluctant to include safety measures in their cars, and also accuse them of saying that there are no unsafe cars, only unsafe drivers.

But we really know very little about these things, and there is much difference of opinion about them. As Mackay points out, there are three different sets of regulations covering vehicle lights, those in the U.S.A., the Continent of Europe, and in Great Britain, with France odd man out in insisting on yellow headlamp glass. There is no unanimity about these things, or about other 'safety' features, and most of them depend on hunches, not on knowledge. The RRL have shown that there is little to be said for the yellow glass, but that is about as far as we have got. Which of them is right?

A British car maker fitted flashing direction indicators to all his cars in the late twenties or early thirties. They were good, and quite a promising idea, but a Committee was set up by the Minister, which decided against the flashing lights, and, without making any tests, and on mere hunch, recommended the useless and inefficient 'trafficator'. It took some years, and the re-introduction of the flashing lights from the U.S.A., to get them made legal here. The car maker concerned lost a lot of money, although his idea was right, and the Committee's wrong, and may, indeed, have helped to cause accidents.

Is it reasonable to expect manufacturers to scrap a model on which they have spent large sums of money unless there is very clear evidence that it is dangerous, and that the danger is really important? There might be some dangerous feature in an otherwise excellent car which only becomes serious under very rare and exceptional conditions.

Part of the trouble is also that some of the people who are throwing stones at the manufacturers live in very brittle glasshouses themselves. Mrs Castle and Senator Ribicoff had some responsibility for the roads. We do know, on such evidence, that there is no room for any reasonable doubt, that the roads are large contributors to accidents, and those who say the car makers should design safe cars are forgetting that many of the accidents would not have happened at all if the roads had been up to modern standards.

The effect of car design on accidents is a subject on which we still have much to learn, though some progress has been made. Once again, the study made has been unco-ordinated, and much of it seems contradictory.

3. ALCOHOL

This is a matter on which we must be specially careful to be objective. We have here the two things—the motor and alcohol—which have attracted to themselves more prejudice than any other two things in the national life, and in their conjunction it is exceedingly hard to be impartial. On alcohol specially, Chambers's 'hairy Esaus' are particularly active.

Pole has discussed the matter in some detail, and I will confine myself to one or two comments, and to discussing an important statistical point.

There is a large volume of research on the matter, but most of it is weakened by its concentration on what *could* or *might* cause accidents, and not on what *does* cause them. The two former things, after all, are only based on someone's hunch, and may not be important. It is just assumed that if any driver involved in an accident had been drinking, argal his drinking *caused* that accident. Even Borkenstein, in 'Grand Rapids', who did study whether alcohol *does* cause accidents,* made this assumption, which is by no means always valid. As the Warmwell Cross incident showed, we cannot always be sure that factors other than the drink were not more important.

In this country, the fatalities over the Christmas weekend are claimed as 'proof' that drink plays a large part in accidents. But they are always presented in misleading form. The important figure is not the total number of deaths that weekend, but the extra number over the normal mean daily number. The Press and BBC announcements are misleading, and make some people think that there are no deaths at all except at holiday times. The extra number in 1963 was about 50, not the total of 132.

Table 2 (p. 21) sets out the times of deaths that weekend. Those after 10 p.m. (22.00 hrs) are usually said to be the decisive proof that drink was involved. But it is also usually forgotten—or ignored—that large numbers of people travel to attend midnight religious services on that night, alone of all others throughout the year. At Buckfast Abbey, near where I live, a large car park which normally holds 100 cars with ease is jammed tight with them for the Christmas Midnight Mass from about 11 p.m. till between 1 and 2 a.m. This is also the case at many other churches throughout the country. This extra traffic must surely have caused some deaths. The RRL report said that this extra traffic was not recorded, but it is largely local, and might not pass the census points.

Another point mentioned in the Report, but which got little publicity, is that in about one-fifth of the Christmas deaths, the *pedestrian* concerned in the accident had been drinking and *not the driver.* Some of these had fantastic amounts of alcohol in the blood. One had 370mg%, another 327, and a third 239.

To what extent is the drinking-driver a real problem? Borkenstein, in the 'Grand Rapids' study, estimated that if all *drivers* kept their blood-alcohol level below 80mg%—our legal level—the number involved in accidents would fall by about 6%. His figures are, as I have said, marred by the assumption that if a driver had been drinking, argal he was responsible for the accident.

---

* This study has recently been discussed in RRL Report No.6, 'Alcohol and Road Accidents' by R. E. Allsop, RRL, 1966.

This assumption is not valid, so his estimate may be on the high side.

The 1967 White Paper estimates (Section 28, p. 10) that the new Act will save between 150 and 240 deaths per year. This is largely guesswork, and is again based on the same assumption, so it may be too sanguine. There is also no sign that the Minister has set the lives saved against the deaths which the Act will cause. The implementation of the Act will cost a vast sum of money in publicity—a third of a million—Breathalysers, tests, time of the police and courts, and so on. In the way things are worked, this will be taken from the money allotted to roads, so that some improvements will be deferred, and people killed as a result. These deaths should be set off against any saved by the Act. Neither, of course, has the Minister counted the lives which will be lost in the future due to the suspension of licences, nor the social damage caused by the edifying sight of the courts solemnly punishing a man for impairing his driving by themselves impairing his driving.

As an example of what I mean, there is a crossroads in the Midlands where four people were killed in 1967. The local authority has been pressing for a roundabout, which would almost certainly have saved those lives (Table 10, p. 46, Table 13, p. 57, and Table 14, p. 68), but cannot get the money. If this is being withheld because it is needed for the publicity for the Act, then the lives lost at this place in 1968 should count against the saving in lives the Act makes.

Pole says (11.7, p. 147) that the new Act is perhaps the fairest way of dealing with what is so often called the 'drunken driver',* but there is a statistical point which may lead to some doubt. I must bring in some figures here, and can only ask the nonmathematical reader to take them on trust.

As I have already said, no matter how scientific a measurement may be, it cannot be exact, and must be subject to error variations. In the blood-alcohol test, these are likely to be due to (a) uneven distribution of the alcohol in the blood-stream (11.8, p. 151), and (b) errors in the machine and by the operator. As Pole says (*ibid* p. 151), the Swedish estimate of the standard deviation is 5 mg%.

---

* Another pejorative term.

He also says that the new gas chromatography apparatus has an s.d. of less than 2mg%, but this does not include the uneven distribution, so the overall value of the s.d. may still be about 5mg%. If it is not, it still does not affect the principle of what follows, only the figure. I will assume the value of 5 mg% and that a single test is made.

If the driver has an exact mean of 80, the variations will involve an even chance of his being found to be either over or under the 80. The court, then, could dispense with the test, and toss a coin to decide his guilt.

If his *real* mean content is 75, one test out of six will find him to be over the 80, and correspondingly if his real mean was 85, one test in six would make him below the 80. In such a case, then, the court could throw a six-sided die to decide his guilt or innocence.

If his real mean is 70, the variations will mean that one test in about 40 will find him over the 80, or if it is 90, then he will be found to be below the 80 once in 40 tests.

In practice it is not as easy as that. We never know the exact mean, and, if the laboratory says that he has 85mg% in his blood as a result of a single test, his real mean may vary from 75 to 100mg%, or even more widely.

If, as Pole says will be done, two samples are taken, this does not halve the error, but would have the effect of reducing the s. d. to 3.5, and if the accused's third sample is taken into account, this figure would become about 3, and leave the principle unchanged.* This is why in Sweden, as mentioned by Pole (11.8, p. 151) the laboratories only report when the result is 15mg% above the legal limit, or in this country with the new method, it is proposed to report 6mg% above the limit. Both are based on three standard deviations. The 6mg% may not be enough margin because it only allows for machine errors and not those of distribution. This procedure might meet the objection to some extent, but we have yet to find out what the courts will make of it. It still leaves some objection because any errors will favour the guilty, and penalize the innocent, and the whole thing seems to me to be at odds with what is always said to be one of the

---

* This is a somewhat technical matter. The explanation which involves some mathematics, will be be found in the Appendix (p.223).

fundamental principles of English Law, that the court should be satisfied of the defendant's guilt beyond any reasonable doubt.

Returning to the question of whether there is a serious problem, this certainly does not seem to be established on a really solid ground of evidence. Allgaier and Yaksich (3.11, p. 29) did not find that the consumption of alcohol in a state seriously affected its death rate. There is theoretically much difference among the states, some of them being 'dry', though I must partly destroy my own case by pointing out that that might not affect the consumption of alcohol in the state, and judging from what I saw under Prohibition it might even increase it. It is, however, probable that there is some problem.

The next question is how best to deal with it. I feel strong doubts on the value of prosecutions, and also on the value of the 'Don't drink and drive' slogan. There is an old, and very true, saying 'The best is the enemy of the good', and this may apply here. The slogan may set out the best, but is it asking too much of the ordinary man, and setting too high a standard? Is it even really necessary? As Pole has said (11.7, p. 149), there is evidence that small amounts of alcohol, say a pint of beer, are harmless, and there is no evidence that they are associated with accidents.

It is argued that even small amounts of alcohol impair a man's driving by increasing his reaction time. We do not really know how important this is. In all probability, most drivers only use the full limit of their reaction time once in a blue moon, so it may not matter very much. In any case, we encourage the courts to impair people's driving, so that does not really worry us.

It may be, then, that we are asking people to accept an unnecessarily high standard, and that some lesser ideal would be more effective by reducing the demand on human nature. Complete prohibition of alcohol has always been a failure wherever it has been done because it asks too much. I saw it in the U.S.A. as a young man, and it impressed itself on my mind. In Norway, a semi-prohibition country often held up to us as an example, I once had to park my car, switch off the engine, and tell my passengers not to speak while the drunkest man I have ever seen in my life lurched by on foot. I could only hope that he would not lurch into the car. The previous evening my wife had been annoyed in the street by a drunken man. Nothing like that has ever occurred to us anywhere else.

To summarize—the questions to which we need answers are:

(*a*) To what extent is drink a serious problem in connection with accidents?

(*b*) Are strict legislation and severe penalties the best way of dealing with it?

(*c*) Can we tolerate a method of dealing with it which introduces an element of chance, even of gambling, into the law?

(*d*) Are our present methods of dealing with it doing more harm than good? Are the social dangers of the penalties more important than the problematical benefits that they bring in by the reduction, if any, in accidents?

(This section was written late in 1967. See also Epilogue, p. 219.)

4. THE DRIVER

M. le Préfet (Qu. 10, p. 103) says that *all* accidents are caused by 'lunatic' and murderous drivers, and Mr Fleming (Qu. 11, p. 103) says much the same thing. They express the conventional opinion, but it does not seem to occur to them that a driver is not always present at the accident (3.5, p. 19).

What evidence is there for this idea? Only the *obiter dicta* of eminent men, none of whom is qualified by knowledge to speak on the subject, not even Mr Fleming (Qu. 11, p. 103) who, as a policeman and not a traffic engineer, sees only one side of the question.

There is a small, but better informed, body of opinion which thinks differently:

(16) 'On the other hand, the existence of dangerous drivers appears to be debatable.'*

---

* Bulletin de l' Association Internationale Permanante des Congrés de la Route, 51° Année, 1er Trimestre 1962. No. 165. This publication is the journal of the Permanent International Association of Road Congresses, of which road engineers in most countries in the world are members. It is published in English and French. The quotation is from the English version.

This quotation is from a Report on the papers presented for *Theme IV,* 'Research into Road Traffic Accidents' of the World Traffic Engineering Conference, held at Washington from 21 to 26 August 1961. The principal reporter was M. Coquand, Director of Roads and Road Traffic, France,* and the Committee of Reporters included some of the world's most distinguished traffic engineers.

In the Annual Report of the Bureau of Public Roads of the U.S.A., as reported in TEC, are these words (TEC, September 1967):

> (17) 'The belief that a large percentage of accidents is caused by a group of careless or dangerous persons, appears to be untrue. The truth, according to research investigations, is that most drivers perform "as well as can be expected, but face difficult combinations of road traffic situations and vehicle operation requirements".'

The opinions of such knowledgeable persons must demand some consideration. If they are right, and the conventional opinion wrong, then it becomes very clear that we must do some fresh thinking.

What is dangerous driving? Fitzgerald has discussed this in Chapter 12.1 (p. 159) from the legal angle. The courts have now virtually defined it as any conduct leading to an accident. From the traffic engineer's angle, this is more of Hamlet's miching mallecho. There is all the world of difference between really deliberate recklessness, and the kind of thing which happened at Warmwell Cross, when drivers, doing their best, fell into a trap set by the road conditions. One or two of these people were convicted of 'killing by dangerous driving'. As a result of the prosecutions, I was unable to find out what the trap was. Who was 'behaving' dangerously here, the driver—or the courts?

I would strictly limit the term 'dangerous driving' to really deliberate recklessness, and I interpret quotations 16 and 17 in the same sense. I do not think this is a serious matter, it happens so seldom. But, falling into traps, errors of judgement, carelessness, incompetence, frustration, lack of consideration for others, and so

---

* cf (Qu. 10, p. 103), We may well ponder whether the Director of Roads, or M. le Préfet, is in the best position to know most about the subject.

on, are failings common to all human beings, and dealing with them is a very different matter from dealing with wilful recklessness. Some of them can be prevented by altering the road to remove the traps, to direct the incompetent into the right way, or remove the frustration. Penalties are, at best, useless as a remedy for them, and at worst, very harmful.

It seems probable that, on the whole, we have an easier problem to deal with in this country than in most. Most foreign traffic engineers say that the standard of driving, and especially of consideration for others, is higher in this country than in any other. In Germany and Australia it has even been suggested that applicants for driving licences in those countries should be compelled to train in driving here to learn how to behave. I pass this on to the Government as a help to exports.

One conclusion may perhaps follow from the results of the study outlined in Chapter 3.9. Countries with the left-hand rule of the road seem consistently to have two-thirds of the deaths which right-hand rule countries are expected to have. I cannot account for this, but state what may, perhaps, be a fact. It might be due to some psychological effect on the drivers. We shall have some confirmation, or otherwise, of this in Sweden which has changed its rule, though it will take time—perhaps two or three years—to show whether it is permanent. If it is, we would expect the deaths in Sweden to rise by about five hundred per year at once, the number rising as the population and number of motor vehicles in Sweden increases. Until some confirmation or disproof of the proposition could be found, it would be most unwise for us even to think of our changing our rule of the road; it might cost us four thousand lives a year. If it is not correct, we must find some other explanation for what seems to be a remarkable coincidence.

A matter on which we know very little is the effect of experience. Its importance will appear later. There is much reason to think that a man with long experience is a better driver, and it may be that the effect of it is shown in Figures 2 and 3 (pp. 31 & 32), which show that the lowest proportions of drivers involved in accidents are at ages at which performance is usually thought to fall off. This introduces the question of age for driving, also one on which we know very little.

This applies in two ways, the age at which to start, and the age at which we should stop. Pole (11.2, p. 136) queries whether seventeen is the right age at which to start driving. Is it too early or too late? It is not impossible that it would be better to start younger. Some states in the U.S.A. allow driving at fourteen, and do not seem to be the worse for it. There is always much to be said for learning anything early. This is a point which needs study. There is frustration among the young at not being allowed to drive, and some appear to do so without a licence, and so become 'criminals'. Allowing a licence earlier, if necessary with some restrictions on the type of vehicle, might improve driving, and reduce much of this frustration and 'criminal' behaviour.

It is argued that accidents are very high among the young, and Figures 2 and 3 seem to confirm this, but is this high rate due to youth or to lack of experience? It may be that it would be similar in the first year of driving, irrespective of the age at which this is allowed.

We encourage the young to take risks in many ways, in sport of all kinds, mountaineering, and so on, and this is another example of our ambivalence on the matter of road accidents. When a number of young people were killed in a Yorkshire pothole recently, there was no great outcry, yet if they had been killed in a road accident, that would have been an appalling matter. Yet if we encourage people to disregard danger in other ways, we can hardly be surprised if they do it on the road.

At the other end of the scale it is often suggested that the older drivers should be made to take a test at seventy or over. Figures 2 and 3 seem to suggest that the older driver is not a menace. There might be something to be said for a medical test, but we should not lightly take away anyone's licence, still less that of old people, who have more need to drive as they cannot walk so much.

I digress here to give a personal experience. I lost a leg in the First World War. In the early twenties it was said that the limbless were 'obviously' unfit to drive, and should be refused licences. A number of us got together, founded the Disabled Drivers' Motor Club, and showed that we could drive. If the proposal had gone through, many lives and careers might have been severely restricted—mine included—to very little purpose in saving accidents. There is no real evidence that disabled people are unsafe drivers. It is just another hunch, and another example of the irresponsible approach.

Driver-training is often suggested as a means of saving many accidents. It seems an attractive idea, but is there any evidence that it would be a useful one? What little evidence we have tends to show that it would not. Once again, Allgaier and Yaksich found that the standard of driver-education had no effect on the death rates in states which had it. Moreover, there does not seem to be any reason to think that our own highly trained police drivers, whose training—and behaviour—is always held up to us as a model, have a very much lower accident rate than the untrained groundlings. We do not know what the latter's rate is. The 1967 White Paper's estimate was that they have an accident—type, rather typically, unspecified—in 300,000 miles,* but many minor accidents are not reported, so the real rate is more than that. It was recently reported in the Press that the police rate was one 'blameworthy' accident in 66,000 miles. Allowing for the general uncertainty, and difficulties of definition—what is a 'blameworthy' accident? We know that all the groundlings' accidents are automatically blameworthy, does this apply to the police?—the two rates may be thought to be comparable.

The training would be enormously costly, and it is more than probable that the money could be better spent in other ways, and save more accidents.

My last question on this matter will be thought quite shocking. Is the driving test itself of any value? We do not really know, and once again it merely rests on the hunches of eminent men.

5. THE PEDESTRIAN

Very many of the remarks made about the driver apply also to the pedestrian. He is human, with the failings that that term implies. He is reckless, or careless, and makes mistakes. He is also, from the accident standpoint, *the fastest road-user.* This is because

---

* From other data this almost certainly refers to injury accidents. A recent RRL report, LR 79 'Cost of Road Accidents in Great Britain', estimates that there are six damage-only accidents to one injury accident. This would mean that the groundlings have one accident in 50,000 miles. See also 13.6, p. 189.

he can move at right angles to the other traffic. He can create a potential accident situation by making one single step into the carriageway, certainly with two. He can accelerate from rest so quickly that the motorist or cyclist, with their relatively low acceleration and manoeuvrability, can do very little about the situation. The accident may not happen to him because the almost instinctive reaction on the part of the driver is to swerve, and in doing so he may endanger himself and others. We are, of course, always told that the motorist has 'charge of the lethal weapon' but when a pedestrian steps out without care, he takes over part at least of the control of the lethal weapon.

We are also told that the motorist 'must take the factor of carelessness on the part of the pedestrian into account' as Goodhart has put it, but there is a limit to what the motorist can do. He also is bound by his human limitations—and by Newton's Laws of Motion—and if the pedestrian is to have full licence to behave as he pleases, and if the motorist is to bear complete responsibility for any consequences, then the only thing the motorist can do to prevent accidents is lock his vehicle away, and not use it.

There is evidence that pedestrian error is a large factor in accidents. In a recent study made in the City of London, it was found that in 379 accidents involving pedestrians in the City motorists were only wholly responsible for 17, while in another 180, nearly half the number, the pedestrians were to blame.

The results of the Birmingham study were not inconsistent with this. In the Report it is said:

> (18) 'Pedestrians showed significantly more failures than the other road-users, and the majority of those failures were omission. For drivers, the most common type of failure was that of judgement.' (BIR.4, p. 259.)

In New York, it was found that the imposition and enforcement of regulations imposing discipline on pedestrians saved 100 lives per year. That was in a city which already had much better pedestrian discipline than in any of our cities (cf. Table 8, p. 30).

Here, again, I am not attributing blame. It is unfortunate that the word was used in the London study. I would prefer to say that error on the part of pedestrians is an important factor in accidents, and leave it at that.

It is said that estimates of pedestrians' errors are inaccurate, because very often they are not in a position to give evidence on their own behalf. There may be something in this, but people who talk like this go on to destroy their own case, by attributing all blame to the driver, who also is very often not in a position to give evidence on his own behalf. They also forget that much of the evidence against a motorist is violently prejudiced—and that they themselves have done much to create this prejudice.

6. THE LAW

The most important of all the questions we must ask is whether the present law stops accidents, or whether its sole purpose is to punish the motorist. This latter part of the question is, of course, a treasonable thought, but there is much evidence that it is the truth.

Before discussing this further, I must deal briefly with two matters. The first seems a detail, but it has important implications for the traffic engineer. It is the 'absolute penalty'. Fitzgerald has discussed this in principle, but not in its practical effects. These are illustrated by Warmwell Cross (6.11, p. 64) and by another accident spot I had to study. Once again, we could not understand why drivers disregarded a Halt sign. Then, happening to pass one day, I noticed a large van parked in front of it. On inquiry it was found that the driver was in the habit of doing this at irregular intervals when making calls at a near-by shop.* Whether this was the cause of the accidents or not, I do not know, but it is not improbable, especially combined with the facts that the motorist was on a diversion of an important trunk road which normally had priority, so he would not expect a Halt sign, and that, once again, the road surface was convex upwards, so that he would not see the Halt line until almost on top of it. Another pretty little trap.

When an accident occurred, all the police had to do was to prove that Mr X had passed the Halt sign. He had then broken a law, and so would be presumed responsible for the accident. It was

---

* A similar incident is described, with a photograph, in the Report on the Birmingham Study. (BIR.4, p. 97 ff.)

189

up to him, and not to the police to show that the sign was hidden, but until the concealment of the sign was found out and remedied, we could not expect the accidents to stop.

Much the same thing happened at Warmwell Cross. The prosecutions hid the trap. The question we may ask, then, is how many accidents and deaths have been due to the absolute penalty? Probably very many.

The next matter is *impairment*. What does it mean? A reasonable interpretation, which makes the matter clearer, would be to say that a man's driving is impaired if he has increased the probability of his having an accident, and I shall use it in that sense. On the actual statistical probability, Garwood has said that the average chance of a private car being involved in a *personal injury* accident, under average conditions, is about 1 in 450,000 per mile travelled.* Borkenstein, in the 'Grand Rapids' study, estimated the effect of the 80mg% blood-alcohol content as doubling the probability of having an accident. Parliament has decided that this amount of impairment—perhaps from one in 450,000 to one in 225,000—is a very serious crime—for a motorist.

The fundamental idea behind the present law, is that a deterrent is needed to deter the 'dangerous driver', and this is very generally accepted (Qus. 6, 8, 9, 10, pp. 102 & 103) and almost any newspaper almost any day). This assumes that all accidents are due to wilfully dangerous behaviour on the part of the motorist, an idea which we have seen is open to much doubt.

But is a deterrent effective? Many people, especially judges, have always maintained that it is, and much of our penal law depends on that assumption. But there has been a rather smaller, and perhaps more enlightened, school of thought, which doubts this. The first case I have come across in my reading was the speech of Diodotus the son of Eucrates in the Athenian Assembly in 428 B.C.—rather a long time ago—as reported by Thucydides. Sir Thomas More also cast doubts on it in the first book of *Utopia*—written 1510–20—which is always thought to have expressed his own opinions. He queried the value of hanging people for theft—a common case of the reactionary being years ahead of his times. His doubts did not

---

* See 13.4, p. 184. This illustrates the degree of uncertainty in these matters.

become current thought till late in the eighteenth century. Between his age and then, the penalties steadily became more and more severe, until finally people were hanged for quite trivial thefts. We have now abolished capital punishment even for murder, and whether we are worse off still seems controversial, but if we are it is not on a very large scale. The general tendency has been for penalties to get lighter, except for motorists, for whom they are getting stiffer and stiffer.

There is, of course, a built-in deterrent already—the accident itself—so the legal one is an extra. Only the maddest of the lunatic fringe would claim that motorists enjoy having an accident, so is another deterrent likely to have much real effect over and above that inherent in the accident itself?

But, of course, if most accidents happen to drivers who are honestly doing their best, but that best has failed either through incompetence, or human failing, or a trap in the road conditions, or through the conditions presenting too difficult a problem for the fallible human being (Qu. 17, p. 184) then the deterrent idea may become entirely wrong. To try to deter a man from doing his best does not seem very sound, and to deter a man from driving prudently (8.2, p. 94) is raving lunacy.

In any event, accidents are often all over in a fraction of a second and no one has time to think about the deterrent. On all counts, the value of the deterrent, except in a few cases, becomes very doubtful.

There is an almost universal consensus of opinion that the suspension of a driving licence is the best penalty or deterrent. I am swimming against the stream when I say that this is very much a matter of doubt. Once again, it all depends on the hunches of eminent men, and no one has ever produced any facts in support of these opinions. It is the most severe *penalty,* but then we first have to establish that a penalty is the best way of stopping accidents. It probably is not, and may even be the best way of causing more.

We do know that in any human activity needing skill, constant practice is essential. Driving is certainly an activity needing skill. Is there, therefore, any reason to doubt that practice is essential for it? To deprive a man of his licence is almost sure to impair his subsequent driving to some extent. The all-important question, then, is whether the deterrent effect, or the impairment effect, is the more effective of the two. As the value of the deterrent is itself a matter of doubt, it may well be that the impairment effect is the more important, and outweighs the deterrent.

We do not do this in other activities. If a ship's master, or officer, or an engine driver, is found to have been careless, we do not usually stop him practising. He may be 'demoted' and given less responsibility for a time. Some years ago, when an air pilot, who had had an accident, and survived it, was dismissed by the airline employing him for alleged error of judgement, public opinion thought that he had been badly treated, and doubted the inquiry. A Commission was even set up to consider the matter of inquiries into air accidents.

Several studies have shown that drivers with less experience are more liable to have accidents, and Borkenstein in 'Grand Rapids' found that drivers with low annual mileages were over-represented in the accidents. It will also be seen from Figure 12 (p. 84) that the increased number of suspensions in Connecticut made no effect at all on the death rate trend in the State, and that it has had no effect on the later rise in the trend. There is, therefore, room for doubt on the value of suspension of licence.

Legislation is very urgently needed to abolish the suspension of licences, at the very least for non-driving offences—that is, those not immediately concerned with the control of a car, such as taking away, or driving while disqualified, and so on—until we have cleared up the doubt about the impairment effect. There is far too much probability that such suspensions cause accidents. The offences can, after all, be dealt with in other ways, and there is no excuse for running the risk that is involved in the suspensions. Pole has shown how these can be a factor in accidents (11.4, p. 139). To illustrate what I mean, there was some time ago an accident in which several people were killed. The driver found responsible, who was killed, was said to have had a 'shocking record' of motoring offences, and was then driving while disqualified. But the Press gave a list of these offences, and not one of them were of careless or dangerous driving, all were either property offences like taking away, or of disobedience to a court, such as 'driving while disqualified'. If the law took cognizance of moral considerations, and if the coroner's inquest was of the smallest value, ought the latter's verdict to have been *manslaughter against the courts which took away the licence?* I throw this out as a question. It is not frivolous. Surely sauce for the motoring goose is sauce for the legal gander, and if the involuntary creation, in ignorance, of an accident situation is a grave offence for a motorist it should be so for a court.

My own personal view is that a driving licence should never be suspended except when it can be very clearly proved, beyond any reasonable doubt, that a man is incapable of driving—such cases as chronic alcoholics or drug-addicts—when it should be for life. Any court which suspends a licence for a limited time, a year or so, takes on itself a very heavy responsibility. To suspend a licence for long periods such as seven years, as is sometimes done, is, I think, in every way as criminal as dangerous driving.

There are other grave objections to the motoring law, based on general principles but having a practical effect. There is every reason to think that in many courts a motorist is already convicted and sentenced before the hearing. He is presumed to be automatically guilty. I have seen an instance of this when a Judge had clearly made up his mind the defendant was guilty, and made no secret of the fact. The Bow Group panel, who wrote the pamphlet *The Scales of Justice,* said that this was a general practice in the courts. Coming from a panel of practising lawyers, a profession not given to self-criticism, and from men of a political bent inclining them to favour existing institutions, this is a very strong indictment indeed. The courts confirm the public attitude that the motorist is always responsible.

A similar effect on public opinion, and one making for accidents, is produced by the fact that motorists are prosecuted and punished severely for acts which are not criminal at all when done by others. Thus, there is no general offence of killing by dangerous *conduct,* only of killing by dangerous *driving.* Some years ago a motorist driving with inadequate lights ran down and killed some pedestrians. He was severely punished. At about the same time a cyclist, also driving with inadequate lights, ran down and killed a pedestrian. He was not prosecuted, but if he had had a tiny engine on his bicycle he could have been. One frequently sees reports in the Press of deaths which appear to be due to someone's reckless conduct, but which are not followed by prosecution. Thus the support of the law is again giving the idea that the driver, and the driver only, is wholly responsible for accidents.

When one reads the reports in the Press of prosecutions in the courts for motoring offences, one wonders what value these can possibly be. Many of them look so futile. I cannot help thinking that they do far more harm than good, and that in many cases they have an anti-deterrent effect, so to speak. That is, when X and Y have had an accident together, if left alone, each may have a lurking feeling at the back of his mind that he was at fault to some extent, and must mend his ways. It is rare for one participant to be wholly at fault. But the Police then prosecute X, and use Y as prosecution witness. Y will feel that he was wholly in the right, and any possible deterrent effect of the accident is destroyed for him. X knows that Y was to some extent at fault, and feels a grievance that he was the only one prosecuted, and may come to feel that he has been badly treated and that Y was the real culprit, so the deterrent effect is at least partly reduced for him, and the prosecution has done harm all round.

But the evil effect of the prosecution does not end there. Both X and Y might have had some evidence of real value to give to the traffic engineer who wants to find out what the traps are in the road conditions which led to the accident. The police inquire into it, and the object of this is merely to find out if a case can be made against X. Why he did what he did is irrelevant to the inquiry. I have given cases of this happening, and need not pursue the subject. But the effect on the motorist is that, being human, he is out to *muddy the wells of inquiry with the stick of precaution* like Mahbub Ali in the Kasmir Serai in *Kim,* and the vital information which would enable us to stop more accidents may be hidden from us.

An illustration of what happens is an accident at one of the bends included in the sample for line 10 of Table 10 (p. 46). I can vouch for the complete truth of this. A motorist came round one of these bends on a showery morning in spring. He seemed to have skidded and he collided with another car. His passenger was killed and he was seriously injured. He was charged with killing by dangerous driving, and the jury acquitted him. No doubt the judge fumed at what he would call a 'perverse verdict'.

Shortly afterwards the bend was dressed, and the accidents

stopped. Some time later, the county surveyor was told that two roadmen had arrived immediately after the accident—though they had not seen it—and helped the victims. The police arrived some time later when the road had dried, and the roadmen told them that, at the time of the accident, *the wet surface had been almost too slippery to stand on.* The police pooh-poohed the idea, and the slipperiness was not mentioned in court. The jury were right, but if a judge had been sitting without a jury the defendant would probably have been convicted.

Note the results of the law and the propaganda. *We must not blame the police,* they are as indoctrinated by the propaganda as we are, possibly far more so. But vital information was withheld from the court, and, *far more important, from the county surveyor.* He had dressed the surface as an experiment. If he had not done so, no doubt more lives would have been lost, for which surely the responsibility would have rested on the law and the propaganda. Was the jury's verdict perverse, or would a judge's have been?

On many grounds, of which I have only given a few, I feel that the law is as bad from the practical point of view as it is on the grounds on which Fitzgerald has criticized it. I would even go further. *If I was commissioned to produce a code of law designed to cause accidents without its purpose being too blatantly obvious, I do not feel that I could very much 'improve' on the present code, and would not suggest much modification of it.*

In this chapter, I have shown a few of the many questions to which we must find answers before we start stopping accidents. I could fill the book with them.

14

BLAME

'How is it that thou canst see the speck of dust which is in thy brother's eye, and art not aware of the beam which is in thy own? By what right wilt thou say to thy brother, Wait, let me rid thy eye of that speck, when there is a beam all the while in thy own? Thou hypocrite, take the beam out of thy own eye first, and so thou shalt have clear sight to rid thy brother's of the speck.'

Matthew 7, verses 3–5. Trans. R. A. Knox

'How hast thou merited—
Of all man's clotted clay the dingiest clot?'

Francis Thompson, The Hound of Heaven

WE have now reached the stage when we can consider blame, but this chapter will be brief. I discuss the whole subject with distaste, but I cannot avoid it. It is the foundation of the present approach to the problem.

The attribution of blame is the main reason why we have so many accidents. Everyone—governments, ministers, legislators, judges, propagandists, the public—all rush to blame the motorist, and, having done so, lean back and say: 'I thank God I am not as other men, murderers, drunkards, selfish, impatient, as also are these motorists' to alter the Pharisee's prayer in Luke 18, verse 11.

I most certainly would not say that no blame attaches to the motorist. But since everyone blames and abuses him, I need not labour the point. I think this blame is overdone but, nevertheless, there is truth in it. But, having conceded the point, we may now ask some questions.

Does the fact that one person is to blame mean that no one else is? Surely no one in his senses can claim that that is so. Then, again, can one claim that an action which is blameworthy, in principle, in the motorist, is not so in anyone else? If it is wrong for a motorist to be impatient when that impatience causes risk to the lives of others, is it not wrong for someone else to do the same thing? Surely it must be.

All the things for which the motorist is blamed are done by others, and many lives are lost as a result. Can one deny that many of the accidents in activities other than motoring are also due to someone's fault or error? They clearly are, yet no one blames them.

Why not? If human characteristics are blameworthy in one case, surely they are in others.

The motorist is specially blamed for lack of consideration for others. Yet what consideration does he receive? Legislatures pass laws without giving thought to their effect on the motorist, and without bothering in any way to study whether they have any effect on accidents. Someone suggests restrictions on motorists without ever even checking—or even bothering—whether they are likely to be effective. It does not matter—if they go wrong, the result can be blamed on the motorist.

But how can we say, as people in effect do say, that Mr X on his way to the office in the morning, and having cut things fine, is an enemy to the community, if he hurries in his car (Qu. 1, p. 3) along the roads, yet having once parked his car, he then becomes an angel of light if he darts across the road, regardless of anyone else, on his own flat feet in the last few yards of his way to that office? He still remains Mr X, and he still shows the human failings of carelessness, impatience, and so on, but as he has left his car these are looked upon as blameless, and he as having handed over all responsibility to the other X's who are still in their cars. They must not be impatient, but he can be.

Similarly, it is a frightful offence, worthy of the most condign punishment, if he impairs his driving by taking a glass of beer with his lunch—does he impair it? We neither know nor care—but a highly meritorious action in a court impairs his driving for some time by taking away his licence for a mere technicality. Is the court wholly free from blame? The courts will, of course, give the answer of Chief Justice Bereford in the fourteenth century 'it was very mischievous; but since the Law is such, one cannot avoid the mischief'. This surely was also the defence of Eichmann. The courts will claim that they are ignorant of the effect of their activities, but they do not accept the defence of ignorance on the part of an accused motorist.

The cold, hard fact is that we are all to blame, from Job Trotter in the street, upwards. But those most to blame are the Lambaste the Motorist School, the Lords, the Bishops, the Judges, the Legislators, and all who pontificate about the subject when they know nothing about it. They should know better. Even traffic engineers are to some extent to blame for being fools enough to listen to the others. I have made my own confession. I too was one of the fools (6.8, p. 59) though I have at least repented.

But I repeat, the attribution of blame is worse than useless, it is harmful. It stops us from asking the vital question, 'Why did X do what he did?', which we must ask if we are to stop accidents. It even prevents us from wanting to stop the accidents. Everyone is satisfied that all is for the best, in the best of all possible worlds, as long as we punish enough motorists, and punish them severely enough. We even ought to hang them. (Qu. 6, p. 102.)

Let us therefore remember the two quotations at the head of the chapter. We are, each of us—whether Motorist, Pedestrian, Legislator, Bishop, Judge—'of all man's clotted clay the dingiest clot' and we are all busily engaged in taking the speck from the motorist's eye, while disregarding the beam in our own. Even if we are motorists, we do this; it is always the other man who is to blame, not us.

But, let us now forget blame, as I shall do, and discuss it no more. It serves no useful purpose, and can do nothing but harm. Let us now get on to discuss what no one so far, except a few fools of traffic engineers, has ever considered—STOPPING ACCIDENTS.

As Hilaire Belloc said in *The Path to Rome:*

'So, that was an interlude, forget the clamour.'

15

THE NEW APPROACH

'Add this one to the rest.
Take it and try its worth, here dies another day.'

Robert Browning, The Rabbi ben Ezra

1. DO WE WANT TO STOP ACCIDENTS?

It will be thought that I have borrowed the title of this chapter from that lamentable document the 1967 White Paper, *Road Safety—A Fresh Approach,* which would have been so much more appropriately entitled *Road Safety—The Mixture as Before.* But I used it myself in a paper I presented to the Institution of Highway Engineers in 1957, and again in another paper in 1961, so it is surely my property, and I can perhaps thank Mrs Castle for the sincerest form of flattery.

But the question I have asked in the section heading will seem horrible. Of course we want to stop accidents, we talk of nothing else. But do we really? There is much evidence that we do not. To take only one instance, some years ago two traffic engineers, Smeed and myself—Smeed being an authority of the very highest—produced papers, independently, showing that we could halve the accidents. If we really wanted to stop them surely these papers would have aroused interest, and have been investigated. Yet no notice whatever was taken.

The White Paper has admittedly hinted at action on one of my own detail suggestions, the imposition of discipline on pedestrians, but that is as far as it goes. The really important ones are passed over in silence.

There are, I think, two reasons for our subconsciously not being enthusiastic about stopping accidents. The first is that they have developed into what one can reasonably call a racket. There are so many people whose livelihoods depend on them. Mr Fleming gave a list of these in Quotation 12 on page 108, and I need hardly press the point. No blame, we are all like it.

The second is that we are so saturated with the propaganda that we are satisfied that we need do no more than just punish motorists. Smeed and I proposed practical measures which did not involve any punishment or legal sanctions, so it was just taken for granted that they were useless. The Pedestrians Association, and Terrell, with their frequent suggestions for further stiffening the already murderous law, have no difficulty in getting publicity, because people believe in the penalties.

Are we genuinely troubled about the deaths? Probably not. We accept double the number in other types of accident with complete equanimity, and with deafening silence. They do not, after all, provide any excuse for more punishments for motorists, so they are not important.

Now let us start with our new approach, and think how we can start stopping accidents.

2. HOW MANY DEATHS COULD WE SAVE ON THE ROADS?

This has been discussed elsewhere by Smeed and myself. We both arrived at the same result, which was that we could halve the annual number of deaths. The measures we proposed to this end were not the same, though I used some of his figures to supplement mine, his paper having been published while mine was in preparation.

We based our estimates on things which could be done without any really material change in the whole approach, so we did not tackle the real question, which is what we could do if we really tried to do it in a big way, discarding all the old prejudices. If we did that, we could save a very large number indeed.

My estimate of what could be done without very drastic changes, is given in Table 17. In this I have rounded off the figures.

Type of work	Lives saved per year
Modernization of the rural main and trunk roads	1,000
Bypasses & motorways (extra to above)	250
Pedestrian control	500
Street lighting improved to modern standards	500
Miscellaneous, including seat belts, anti-locking brakes, reductions in numbers of two-wheeled vehicles etc.	1,000
Total	3,250

TABLE 17 Possible reduction in fatalities per year

The relegation of seat-belts to a miscellaneous item may be found surprising, in view of the publicity given to them recently, especially by Mrs Castle,* but the Rt Hon. Lady forgot that in many cases the belts merely reduce the effects of accidents which would never have happened at all if her roads had been up to modern standards. They are a palliative, and not a remedy for accidents. Much of the saving in accidents that she claims for the belts are included in the first line of Table 17, so they become a minor factor. This also applies to the possible effects of safety factors in cars which Mrs Castle and Senator Ribicoff thought so important.

The figure I have given in the table for the effect of modernization of the roads is based on an overall estimate from the results given in Table 10 for the civil engineering works in section (*a*) of the table. From this it seems reasonable to think that we could halve the number of deaths on the rural roads—meaning by this those out of the built-up areas—and this would amount to about one thousand lives saved per year. This does not mean turning all the rural lanes into motorways, only bringing the main roads up to modern standards. It also allows for the work already done.

It will at once be said that this is impossibly costly. It certainly would involve the spending of a vast sum of money, but then the present dispensation is also enormously costly, both in accidents and in the cost of traffic congestion. But if we argue like that, we then have to find an answer to the question whether we are punishing motorists to save accidents or to save money. In any case, if we wish to remain a modern nation, and keep our economic position, the work has to be done some time, so the sooner it is done the better.

If is, of course, quite unthinkable that we could eliminate all accidents. There is bound to be a hard core of them due to such things as wilful recklessness—on the part of all road-users—human error, mechanical failure, suicide, and so on. Even the railways, with a century of careful study of accidents, and all their mechanical advantages, have not succeeded in eliminating them. There must be an irreducible minimum below which we cannot

---

* In my family, the seat-belts in my car—which we do use—are called 'Barbara'.

reduce the number of deaths, though it is quite impossible to estimate that number. But, basing it on present figures of population and number of motor vehicles, we might guess that it should be less than half the present number. Perhaps we could put it that the multiplying figure in the Smeed formula (3.9, p. 24ff.) might become about 100, as against the present 250 in this country, or 360 in the countries with right-hand rule of the road. Dare I suggest, however, that study in those countries might indicate that they must change their rule of the road to achieve the figure of 100?

3. THE NEW APPROACH: THE CHANGE OF HEART

In her interview with the *Times* Motoring Correspondent, from which I have already quoted (p. 74), Mrs Castle said that a change of heart was needed on the part of road-users. There would be much truth in what she said, if it was not so restricted. The change of heart must be on the part of *everyone,* and it must start with Ministers and legislators. When they have made their change of heart, stopped giving all their attention to the punishment of motorists, and turned it to stopping accidents, then the rest of us will change our hearts too.

The whole official approach conveys an impression of rather futile and helpless irresponsibility. Mrs Castle in this country (when she was Minister of Transport)—and Senator Ribicoff in the U.S.A.—blamed the motor manufacturers for their lack of attention to safety features in their cars, yet she herself showed no sign of recognition that her roads played a part in accidents. Surely if it is the duty of the manufacturers to make safe cars, it is equally the responsibility of the community—which she represented—to make safe roads for them to travel on. After all, traffic engineers have been telling all Ministers—I only name her because she was Minister at the time of writing—this for thirty years, and they have taken no notice.

Then when we had accidents in fog on the motorways, which got much attention in the Press, an overall speed limit of 70 mile/h was clapped on, though what connection that had with the accidents—it was indeed clearly impossible that it could have had any connection—was never explained, neither was any attempt made to find out how many accidents happen at speeds over 70 mile/h. It was a new restriction on motorists, so that was excuse enough.

Mrs Castle said—with former Ministers—that *you cannot stop all accidents by road improvements,* though, as far as I know, no one has ever said that you can. Yet at the same time, she continued with speed limits, and it is certainly true that you cannot stop all accidents by speed limits. *It is even doubtful whether you can stop any at all with them.* Yet if any evidence could be considered as conclusive, it is that road improvements do materially reduce accidents, while the evidence for speed limits, which she calls conclusive, is shadowy in the extreme.

In the U.S.A., Senator Ribicoff blames the motor manufacturers for blaming drivers instead of themselves. Yet surely they are only following the example set them by Senator Ribicoff, whose speed limit experiment was surely based on the same idea, and which, like the motor manufacturers, with some of the features of their cars said to be dangerous, he persisted in retaining even after it had proved not to be a success.

In France, M. le Préfet blamed 'lunatic drivers', in Sweden the government changed the rule of the road without studying whether it would have any effect on accidents.* Things like this occur all over the world. Legislatures pass the most severe laws bringing in penalties for motorists without the least study of whether these measures will do any good.

Until there is a sense of responsibility in governments and legislatures we can make no progress. The change of heart must start with them, and then it will enter the hearts of men.

I hope it will not be thought that I am too hard on Mrs Castle. To paraphrase Gibbon's famous jibe, I know 'I must not calumniate either Satan or the Minister of Transport'. I am perfectly aware that she was bound by government policy, and limited by the amount of money they provide, which is itself dependent on the national economy. Also that she followed other former Ministers. All I say is that she should have made some

---

* I repeat that I am not saying that the left-hand rule is safer than the right-hand rule, only that the figures show that the possibility exists, and *it was never studied.* I feel sure that the Swedish statisticians would have seen it if they had been asked to study the matter.

recognition of the fact that her roads do bear some large part in accident causation, instead of talking footle like 'you can't stop all accidents', and so on, and bringing in more penalties. If she said to motorists 'I know my roads are partly to blame, do your best, I will do mine' we might have taken her to our hearts.

4. THE NEW APPROACH: RESEARCH

The change of heart must start with a study of *all* the factors associated with accidents. We have here, as all who have read this book with an open mind will realize, a subject of enormous complexity. Pole's chapter alone will show how scrappy and unco-ordinated has been the research. Add all the chapters together, and the result is complete confusion.

Yet the official approach is one of gay over-simplification. It must be part of the change of heart to realize that it is criminal irresponsibility to introduce any measure without the most careful and anxious study of its possible effects. It has hitherto been done merely on the hunches of eminent men who are not qualified by knowledge and always with the idea at the back of the legislative mind—admittedly possibly quite subconsciously—that it *does not matter what we do, if it goes wrong we can blame it on the motorist.*

We do not know why the accidents happen, and we are not making any real effort to find out. Even on the vitally important matter of the effect of the suspension of licences, we are totally ignorant. Yet this is essential and fundamental to the whole of our approach.

It is certain that we can never eliminate accidents completely. We have fallible human nature to deal with. Nevertheless, we can say two things with complete confidence Firstly, there is not the smallest chance of our materially reducing them by our present methods. It is impossible to make people infallible by penalties, however ferocious. *The very idea that we can is lunacy,* yet it is the foundation of our present law. Secondly, *we could very materially reduce the number of accidents if we decided to do it.* But our research must be done with complete objectivity, rejecting all our preconceived ideas and old prejudices.

5. THE NEW APPROACH: THE LAW

The proposals in the White Paper for Road Safety Units, and so on, are quite valueless, especially without the change of heart and the dropping of the old prejudices. The whole idea is throttled at birth by the absence of any proposal in the White Paper to reform the law. Yet, until this is done, we can make no progress at all. Any information gathered—except by the laborious and indirect methods which traffic engineers have been compelled to use up to now—is vitiated by the fact that the witness on whom we must rely for our information, the driver, is not likely to be of any help if the object of the inquiry is to punish him. Being human, he is out to protect himself. Who can blame him? Many people expect him to behave like Zinoviev and Kamenev at their 'trials' in Stalin's purges, and accuse himself of nameless nonsensical and fictional crimes. But that, again, is Hamlet's miching mallecho. It is the last way of finding out the truth, and the best way of concealing it, quite apart from the probable appalling social consequences.

This is, of course, partly due to a fundamental defect in our whole legal system—lawyers pontificate on my subject of traffic engineering, so why should I not do so on their law?—that it is based on the accusatorial system, and not on the inquisitorial. We must, of course, rid ourselves of prejudice due to ancient propaganda about the Spanish Inquisition. The word means 'inquiry', and its principle is that a full inquiry is made into all the circumstances of an alleged crime. In our system, we accuse X of a crime. No real inquiry is made, and the evidence before the court is only what the prosecution and defence think convenient to produce. In the case of the Halt sign I described on page 189, the police did not need to inquire whether the sign was clear, and the defence probably never thought of it. So the accidents went on till I found it out by chance. The implications of this are, of course, far wider than road accidents, but these illustrate the defects in our legal system.

Quite apart from this vital and essential fact that the law prevents our finding out how to stop accidents, it is bad in many other ways, as Fitzgerald has pointed out in his chapter. It concentrates for all practical purposes on the motorist, and so teaches other road-users that they have no responsibility for their own safety, and thus makes the worst possible propaganda. This, in its turn, must affect drivers, since if they have been taught by the highest authority—the majesty of the law—that they are not responsible for their own safety in the earlier part of their career on the road, they are very likely to carry this principle with them to the wheel of a car, and blame others when they themselves are in error. Then, again, by the wholesale and indiscriminate suspension of licences, the law may be impairing the driving of large numbers of people, and by the prohibition of young people driving, it may be helping to create criminals. Does much of our present crime wave arise from the road law?

The words which form the clue are in the Report of the Cairns Committee on Civil Aircraft Accident Investigation:

> (19) '... the object of accident investigation is remedial and not retributive. It is therefore usually more valuable to state the *thing* that was wrong than to identify the *person* who was responsible.' (*The Committee's italics.*)

This admirable principle is followed in aircraft and railway accidents, but not in road accidents. In road accidents the object of the inquiry is only to find out the *person* responsible or, more correctly, to find out the person whom we can find some excuse to blame, and it is totally indifferent to the *thing* which is wrong.

We therefore get things like Warmwell Cross, where it was quite useless to find motorists in the wrong, and then punish them. The only effect this had on the accidents was to make sure that more happened. They could only be stopped—and they were stopped—when the trap was removed.

It is impossible to go into details here, but the law must be changed so as to allow, and help, the research into accident causation. Any practices or regulations which themselves help to cause accidents must also be abolished, so all *absolute* penalties must go, including those concerned with speed limits, stop signs, and double white lines. These things themselves need not be abolished, they can be made advisory. With them must also go the fixed blood-alcohol proportion. It also, of course, means that the inquiry into accidents must have the prevention of accidents, and not the prosecution of motorists, as its sole and only aim.

It will be objected that this means trusting the motorist—which indeed it does—and that he cannot be trusted. But to say this is to condemn the whole nation. The motorist is, in general, drawn from the most trustworthy section of the people. We trust him to run the country, so why not trust him to drive reasonably? We have actually begun to do so by the replacement of so many Halt signs by Give Way signs and, on the whole, we are little the worse.

At present, the principal 'criminal on the road' is the law, and until this 'false and man-made god be dethroned and smashed' (Qu. 9, p. 103) we shall never make any progress in stopping accidents.

6. THE NEW APPROACH: THE TRAFFIC CORPS

We have seen that the whole basis of the new approach is that the reason for the inquiry into accidents should be to prevent accidents, not to punish motorists, and it should be fundamentally research. It follows, therefore, that it cannot remain a police matter. It must be based on traffic engineering and statistical methods, and be highly scientific and specialized and the police are not trained for this. For reasons which will appear later, also, those carrying out the inquiry must be completely independent of the Law Courts, the Highway Authority and the Government. We must, therefore, institute a Traffic Corps, to take over all traffic control, and it is *essential* that they should NOT—repeat NOT—BE A POLICE FORCE. To make them a police force would defeat the whole purpose of the corps, and return us to our present state of unnecessary slaughter. They should be independent, and as impartial, as the Inspectors who carry out the inquiries into railway accidents.

The RRL should also come under the corps. The Lab's takeover by the Ministry was a most retrograde step, and has been harmful to its reputation, as was pointed out by the Estimates Committee of the House of Commons recently. (T, 17.8.67.)

We could put the roads under a public corporation like the railways, in which case the Traffic Corps could then be part of the Ministry of Transport, like the railway inspectorate. Or the roads could continue to be the responsibility of the Government through the Ministry of Transport, and the Traffic Corps could be made a public corporation, devoted to the control of traffic, and the inquiry into accidents.

I see the Corps being looked upon by motorists as friends and helpers, and possibly even taking over some of the functions at present carried out by the motoring organizations. Its manning would have to be partly by trained traffic engineers because they will have to co-operate very closely with the Highway Authority. Its Head would have to be a traffic engineer. The rank-and-file could well be partly recruited from retired police officers, whose early training in sifting and taking evidence would be invaluable. At present, we retire police officers early, when they have some years of useful service before them, and they could thus continue to serve the public in a valuable role, after they had been retrained.

I do not mean by this proposal to cast any aspersions on the police. They have done a job which is fundamentally nothing to do with police functions with great wisdom. The thoroughly bad law which they have had to administer has not completely destroyed the public confidence in them. That in itself is a higher tribute than any I can pay. Unfortunately they and not the legislators get the blame for the bad law.

Fundamentally, traffic control is only a police matter if we look upon punishment as its main purpose. But if our object is to keep the traffic moving with the minimum of inconvenience, delay and danger, it then becomes a traffic engineering matter and must be done by trained specialists.

It will, of course, be said that the controllers of traffic must have police powers, including the power of arrest, but this does not follow at all. We see the patrols of the motoring associations, traffic wardens, or roadmen controlling traffic perfectly well, often better than the police, and being implicitly obeyed by motorists. If the Traffic Corps had the complete confidence of the public they could control traffic even better, because motorists would realize that all was being done in their interests. Naturally, some enforcement will be necessary, but it need only be the same as for other accidents, and the police have general powers which could be used in emergency, but they would seldom be necessary. Even parking control need not be prosecution. One American city uses a large and conspicuous vehicle to remove cars causing obstruction, and the motorist has to pay to recover his car. It is said that the mere appearance of this vehicle clears the streets like magic. Once again, if the corps did this, and was trusted, few would object. Much of the parking difficulty is itself a creation of the law, because we find it easier and cheaper to punish the motorist than to provide adequate car parks.

7. DISCIPLINE

I am not advocating a free-for-all on the roads, with no way of enforcement of discipline. But there is a strong sense of discipline in our people, and I merely suggest using this, instead of, as at present, running against it. Much of the bad discipline which exists, and in spite of what the Bishop of London said (Qu. 1, p. 3) there is really very little, is itself largely due to the present attitude. We blast off at motorists who disregard pedestrian crossings, or traffic lights; but no one stops to think that many of these are almost invisible, and that what we put down to wilful disobedience is just failure to distinguish crossings or lights among all the other garbage in a town. The 'Belisha' Beacon is as near invisible as makes no matter, but no one cares. Just blame the motorist, it is so much easier.

The more laws and regulations you pass, the less people will respect them, and as Fitzgerald says (12.1, p. 157) there are about one thousand regulations, against which a motorist can offend and Mrs Castle was diligently adding to them. How can anyone remember all these? It is impossible. In the days when almost anything was treason, there were constant plots and rebellions. Even worshipping God in garrets, as my own ancestors used to do, was treason. No one then respected such laws, and they do not do it now for the same reason.

But is enforcement of discipline really necessary? We do not attempt to stop other accidents by penalties, and they are far more numerous than those on the roads. Do we, then, need to do so on the road? Do we really think that such discipline is necessary and punishment effective? If we were to make all accidents to be on the same footing, we would either have to remove all penalties on motorists, or increase them for others. What would be the public reaction to that?

There is, however, another approach. It has several times been suggested that *drivers* should be compelled to pay the whole or part of the damage caused to others by their negligence, out of their own pockets, and it has even been claimed that this would stop all accidents. This is again, of course, based on the unfounded assumption that all accidents are the fault of the motorist. If it was adopted, it would not only involve the severest hardship to people who would often be quite innocent, but it would be a magnificent blueprint for more accidents, because it would only confirm others in that fallacious and dangerous idea that they have no part in safety, which is one of the principal accident causal factors in the present law.

The real solution is an extension of this, and if I understand him correctly, was put forward by a Japanese gentleman, Mr Morihiro Matsuda, who had the public spirit to pay a large sum of money for a four-page supplement to *The Times* of 2 November, 1966. His suggestion is too long to quote verbatim, but it can be summed up as being that *everyone whose carelessness or negligence contributes to an accident should pay compensation out of his own pocket.* He included, not only road-users, *but the Highway Authority itself.* This is surely the right solution.

On one occasion, I had to meet a parish where the people demanded a speed limit to 'protect our children'. There was not the slightest need for their children to be on the road. All that was needed was for a small path, which the children already used, to be improved. But after a stormy meeting, we could not reach any conclusion, and I could not convince them in any way. All they did was abuse me for not posting the limit. Finally I pulled out the Ace of Trumps, in the form of an article in the *Listener* (L, 18.4.57) which was a discussion of the case of Lewis *v.* The Carmarthenshire County Council, one which is of much relevance to us. A child in the care of a teacher employed by the County Council ran out into the road, and Lewis, the driver of a passing lorry, was killed in avoiding the child. His widow sued the Council, and obtained substantial damages against them. The article pointed out the doubtful position of a parent if his child caused damage to a motorist. This settled the matter, the path was made the next week without further argument.

It may seem a callous attitude to be more concerned about the loss of money than causing damage to others, but it is not untypical. The danger of their own children was hypothetical, and they realized that they had exaggerated it. But the prospect of large damages being awarded against them was daunting. It would not only hit them but their children as well. It was an excellent deterrent.

I therefore propose that after an accident has been studied by the Traffic Corps, damages should—if appropriate and if a claim is made—be assessed by an impartial body—a court, or a panel of arbitrators—against *anyone* found to have been negligent, whether a driver, a cyclist, a pedestrian, the parents of a child, the owner of animals (12.2 (*b*), p. 169), the motor manufacturer, or the Highway Authority. It would also be important that part, or all, of the damages should be paid by the person or body concerned out of his own pocket, and that he should not be able to cover this by insurance. It could be paid to the person awarded the damages by the insurance company but would then become a debt owing to that company by the person concerned. The amount thus paid by the person would be decided by the court or panel.

It will seem fantastic to suggest that the Highway Authority should be made liable, but surely it is merely following the normal practice in most similar cases, such as an employer, or the State itself in the nationalized industries. The duty is laid on any employer to keep his plant and premises safe, and the courts sometimes seem to put an amazing degree of responsibility on employers. They have been mulcted in damages, or part damages, even when the employee has been grossly reckless, and has quite deliberately disobeyed safety regulations made by the employer.

It is often said that the driver must take the roads as he finds them, and so is always at fault if he has an accident. That is as it may be, and might make the driver partly responsible, but that still does not absolve the community from some responsibility for seeing that there are no traps or dangerous features in the roads. By the same token, it could be said that employees should take the factories as they find them, but the law does not take that attitude. The State provides the roads, and the user has little or no say in the matter. If the motoring associations were to propose to raise money and construct the roads themselves they would get very short shrift from the Government. Surely, then, it is not unreasonable to expect the latter to accept some responsibility for the road conditions.

If an employer had some dangerous feature in his plant, say a slippery floor, and took every possible measure to shift the responsibility for accidents on to his employees, keeping a large organization to that end, and punishing them when they fell, there would be a very strong public reaction when this was found out, and a demand for severe punishment of the employer, and perhaps of his agents. Yet that is exactly what the community is doing on the roads. I have shown how it took us years to find out about the slippery road surfaces, and how the law was the reason for the delay (6.8, p. 60). The agents are the law, and—it must be said—the courts and the police. *They* are applying the law, and the law is preventing our finding out where the traps are, and is passing the whole responsibility to the motorist. Does not this strengthen the reasons for holding that the community should accept some of this responsibility? I am not blaming these people. *They know not what they do.*

Summing up, then, the proposal is that the accident should be studied by the Traffic Corps with the primary aim of research into the prevention of accidents. If any claim for damages is made, a court, or a panel of arbitrators, using their report, would allocate damages to all responsible in any way, and all, or part, of those damages should be defrayed by the individual personally, if the body making the award should so decide, and not out of insurance.

This proposal would go a very long way to stopping accidents, and it might also help to solve another problem, that of the difficulties of the insurance companies. Under the present dispensation they are really insuring two parties, one of whom does not pay any premiums. The motorist is paying everyone's liabilities. Every now and then, it is true, he is awarded damages against a pedestrian, but may not get them in practice. But normally the motorist does not sue a pedestrian, feeling that to do so merely adds legal costs to the rest. There is no reason why pedestrians should not be insured as well. The motorist never gets damages against the highly negligent community.

There is the risk of 'tip-and-run' drivers—and even more likely, pedestrians—trying to evade payment. These could be treated as ordinary criminals, just as if they had tried to evade payment in a shop, but their licences should not be suspended.

The really reckless road-user, the wicked one, could also be dealt with as a criminal, in the same way as we deal with other wickedly reckless persons—if we do. The two latter functions, would, of course, be police matters. If the prosecutions were really confined to the wickedly reckless, then public opinion would look upon them as criminals. Once again, Fitzgerald has discussed this, and I need only add that the answer to Mr Fleming's rhetorical question (Qu. 12, p. 108) is that motorists reported for 'serious' [*sic*] offences, do not look upon themselves as criminals, because they are not criminals. They realize that their 'crime' is being a motorist, and that only.

This proposal does not fully solve the difficulty of people trying to divert responsibility from themselves. It indeed means that everyone might do it. But even if we adopted Fitzgerald's alternative proposal (12.3, p. 175) of dropping all prosecutions, learning to live with the accidents as we do with all others, there would still be the possibility of civil proceedings, so there is even then some risk that the defensive attitude will persist. On the whole, however, it seems likely that if the whole procedure is seen to be scrupulously fair, people will accept it, and the objection may not be very important.

16

REMEDY—OR REVENGE?

'Repay no one evil for evil, but take thought for what is noble in the sight of all. If possible, as far as depends on you, live peaceably with all. Beloved, never avenge yourselves, but leave it to the wrath of God; for it is written: "Vengeance is mine, I will repay," says the Lord.'

St Paul, 12 Romans, verses 17–19

1. THE PROBLEM

This chapter will consist of recapitulation, but before concluding I must discuss one charge which will be made against me, that I am belittling the problem and making it appear less serious than it really is. I am not doing this. I am trying to introduce facts, to state the truth, and to face the consequences of our ignorance—and the reasons for it—on many of the most important aspects of the subject.

Never under any circumstances does one help a case, or solve a problem, by misrepresentation, exaggeration, the use of pejorative words, by misleading propaganda, or by sweeping inconvenient evidence under the carpet. Yet all these things abound in our present approach, indeed it consists of little else. They can do nothing but harm, and I am trying to get rid of them.

First the problem. We have (4.4, p. 36) a new means of transport which has conferred great benefits on mankind, and could confer more, but, owing to prejudice and ignorance, we have not allowed it to do so. But it involves a large number of accidents, partly owing to the great increase in travel which is one of the benefits it has brought.

Here, again, this is not a unique problem. The use of such aids to better living in the home as electricity or gas has also involved similar risks of accident, but we do not hear so much of those.

2. THE PRESENT PREMISE AND ITS RESULTS

Fitzgerald has stated the basic premise behind the present approach (12.3, p. 174) which is, in his words '... accidents don't just happen ... they are caused by the driver ...'

Certain results follow from this. The inquiry into the accident is done by the police with the object—set to them by the law and public opinion—of finding out whether a driver concerned has been at fault. Whether this fault is relevant to the accident is not relevant to the inquiry, neither is the inquiry devoted to stopping similar accidents, except in so far as the punishment of the driver stops them. Once it has been found that the driver has broken a law—and the law is so elastic that it is rarely hard to find this—an armour-plated door clangs to in the mind of everyone—except a few traffic engineers—and the public says, with Caiaphas: 'What further need have we of witnesses?' As in that trial, the mind is firmly closed, the case is pre-judged.

No further study is made of accident causation. It is not even thought that such a study is necessary. So the traffic engineer is prevented from finding out what led to the accident, and from stopping more of the same kind. I have shown (6.11, p. 64) how this has caused more deaths, and that when we tried to find out what happened we were accused of hindering the punishment of motorists. That we were trying to save life counted for nothing against this.

As Pole's chapter shows so clearly, most of the research is devoted to matters of minor importance. He points out (11.6, p. 143) that alcohol '… has very likely produced more research, discussions and suggestions than any other single element in the endeavour to reduce accidents …'. Yet even the Minister, in the White Paper, only claims that the new Act will save between 150 and 240 deaths a year, out of about 8,000. This is chickenfeed, and is fiddling with the fringes of the matter, while leaving thousands to die. My Table 17 (p. 200) shows that we could—we must—make our target the saving of 4,000 lives per year in this country, and Table 6 (p. 27) shows that if the principal motorized countries were to make—and achieve—the same target it would mean the saving of about 50,000 lives a year. This seems a very grisly price to pay for 'allowing ignorance and prejudice to prevent our integrating the motor vehicle into modern life'. (Qu. 5*a*, p. 36.)

A further price we pay for the premise is that we are bringing the law into disrepute. We see everyone, judges, bishops, the directors of the State, the police themselves, down to the mere uncounted folk, treating speed limits with complete contempt, and indeed, most of the motoring law with them. This is made worse by the fact that this contempt for the law is in many cases justified. Each Act stiffens the penalties, without any apparent effect on the obedience to the law. To make matters worse, there is even the possibility that the courts are accessory to the very crimes they are trying, and sometimes are punishing a man for a crime by committing the same crime themselves. We are eroding the very foundations of English Justice, and may even be on the slippery slope leading to the police state.

All these things arise out of the basic premise that all accidents are the fault of the driver, so we must now consider this premise, and set out the things we know, and what we do not know.

3. WHAT WE KNOW

We know, quite beyond argument, that travel accidents happened on a large scale before the motor existed. Probably they were higher relatively to the population a century ago than they are now, in spite of the enormous increase in travel since then.

We also know, again beyond argument, that there are deaths on the road in accidents in which no motor vehicle is concerned.

These two facts alone shake the premise, even without any other evidence.

We also know, on such evidence that no reasonable person could deny it, that road improvements very materially reduce accidents if they are properly done, and not cut down on the grounds of 'economy', and that they may even eliminate fatal accidents. There is strong evidence that they do this by removing traps or by simplifying the problem set to the fallible human being.

4. WHAT WE DO NOT KNOW

The things we do not know are far more important. There are very many fundamental questions to which we need to know the answer, but to which we do not even try to find the answer. I can only deal with the most important ones.

(*a*) Is there any sound basis for the present approach of relying on legal measures intended to punish the motorist, and the motorist only?

(*b*) Is there any foundation for the firm trust in the value of the deterrent?

(*c*) Does suspension of licence make a good deterrent?

(*d*) Does suspension of licence impair a man's driving?

(*e*) If it does, does the impairment effect do more harm to the driving than the deterrent improves it?

The answer most people would give to these questions is to say that they are nonsense, and to dismiss them out of hand. But when we consider them objectively, we see that this attitude rests wholly on hunch. We do not know, but if the answer to (*a*) down to (*c*) is 'No' and to the last two 'Yes', then our whole approach is wrong.

5. WHAT EVIDENCE HAVE WE?

There is some evidence which enables us to answer these. The law is actively harmful in that it prevents the traffic engineer from finding out what the traps are, and removing them. Then there is clear evidence that some at least of the accidents are due to these traps, and the law does nothing to prevent them, and even helps to cause them, because in many of these cases a motorist is honestly doing his best, and the law attempts to deter him by punishing him for doing it.

There is also evidence that error on the part of other road-users plays some part in accidents, and the law does nothing to deter these people from their errors. I am not imputing blame. Road conditions present problems to these others and they are fallible human beings, probably also doing their best. The law may even contribute to these errors by its concentration on the driver. This must teach other road-users that their safety does not depend on themselves but on others. Furthermore, when they become motorists, as so many of them do, this idea that their safety depends on others has become so firmly fixed in their minds that they still believe it. This may account for the very widespread feeling among motorists (Qu. 1, p. 3) that the other man is always responsible for accidents, not me.

It also follows from the premise that the legislators, all over the world, feel that it does not matter what they do, what laws they bring in. If anything goes wrong, they can blame the driver, so they take no care to find out whether their laws are likely to cause accidents.

6. REMEDY—OR REVENGE?

There is therefore room for grave doubt about the efficacy of our present methods. They probably are not effective, and even harmful. This is clearly a matter which needs the closest study. But it does introduce the dilemma that we can only study it by abandoning the whole of our present approach, and concentrating on research.

We are insane on the subject of road accidents, and as a result of that insanity our whole approach is fundamentally wrong, and we are trying to solve the wrong problem. Our law and propaganda are not really based on the wish to stop accidents, but are solely concerned with revenge on the driver, without respect to whether he is guilty. It is thought that this is all we need do to stop accidents. But it is not, it can only cause more, and in this country we are probably sacrificing about four thousand lives a year to this revenge.

We must first realize that the problem is *all* accidents, not just *road* accidents. The human failings which cause the latter are the same as those which cause them in the air, on the railways, at sea, in the home and in industry, yet they are treated quite differently. Only on the road is there this fixation on revenge. In the other cases—except in the home where we are quite indifferent to them— we try to find out why the accident happened, so that we can prevent other similar ones in the future.

Therefore we must have a totally fresh approach, not that of the White Paper, which is no fresh approach at all. We shall never solve the problem of road accidents until we concentrate on REMEDY, and not, as at present, on REVENGE.

> '"... this mine advice, Master More, how think you it would be heard and taken?"
>
> "So God help me, not very thankfully," quoth I. ...'
>
> *Sir Thomas More,* Utopia.
> *First Book. Trans. Ralph Robinson*

EPILOGUE

The main body of the book was written in 1967, and before finally going to press some recent developments may be briefly discussed.

Some more before-and-after studies have come in, but they do not modify anything said previously, including what was said about speed limits. It has also been possible to analyse the death rates for twenty-six motorways in the U.S.A., and also the Pennsylvania Turnpike in more detail since 1940. There is a fairly strong conclusion that the fatality rate on these roads falls off as the traffic increases, and that speed limits do not affect this trend in any way. The differences between the various roads mentioned above (7.8, p. 83) are most probably associated with the differing traffic densities. Our own motorway M1 shows the same trend, and there is no apparent sign that the 70 mile/h speed limit affected this. All this evidence shows no reason to doubt that speed limits on motorways do not affect the fatality rate.

The change in the rule of the road in Sweden seems to have been followed by a reduction in accidents, but latest reports indicate that they may be rising again. It is too early to draw any conclusions, and one must wait until the situation in that country has returned to normal.

The main development is, of course, the Breathalyser. There has been a fall in accidents so far this year, but it is doubtful whether the whole of this can be credited to the Breathalyser. There have been other factors which could help in the reduction of accidents. The tyre regulations were introduced later, but reports of the demand for new tyres showed that many people ordered replacements before the regulations came into force, so the true effect of the regulations is not known. However, to judge from line 10 of Table 10 (p. 46), which shows the great effect of treating slippery roads, it seems certain that these regulations about tyres must have also had some effect in reducing accidents. Another factor may have been a falling off of traffic at night. Reports of this have come in from all over the country, and, as a minor indication, the car park at Buckfast Abbey mentioned above (p. 179) was noticeably less full last Christmas. Yet another factor is said to be that motorists are more reluctant to report accidents to the police. It is not always legally essential to do this, and drivers may be more inclined to settle matters mutually, for fear of the test. If this is so, the reduction in accidents may be partly due to their not being reported, not that they have not happened.

Another important recent development may also have a bearing on the reduction in accidents. Early in the year, the Government announced its cuts in expenditure, and, inevitably, the money allotted to road improvements was the most drastically cut. These cuts can only be applied to the work which saves accidents. No public comment seems to have been made on this aspect of the cuts. Yet we can be fairly confident that they mean that about two hundred people will be killed next year whose lives would have been saved if the cuts had not been made, and that about the same number will die annually until the cuts are restored and the work done. Yet, to illustrate the attitude of helpless irresponsibility mentioned on page 202, Mrs Castle—after having as far as the public could see accepted these cuts—then announced on BBC Television that she was a 'happy woman' because, by an unjustified process of extrapolation, she could claim that the Breathalyser had saved a number of lives. The deaths caused by the cuts, of course, can be—and will be—blamed on motorists, so presumably they do not matter.

The bearing of this on the Breathalyser is that in the last few months a number of road improvements, started before the cuts were made, have been opened to traffic, and they must have reduced accidents, though no account is taken of these. To take examples, the motorway M1 was extended northwards from south of Nottingham to join the Doncaster Bypass almost simultaneously with the introduction of the Breathalyser, and the Severn Bridge was opened a month or two before. These two would be expected to save thirty or so lives a year, at least, and they were just the largest schemes out of many. It would be quite wrong to credit the Breathalyser with the saving of these lives.

This is not to say that the Breathalyser has had no effect; it almost certainly has, but we must not overestimate its effect. We may, however, justifiably ask whether these savings counterbalance its undoubted social harm, especially in its effect on what is said to be the fundamental principle of English Law, that a man's guilt must be proved beyond reasonable doubt. The recent punishment of a man for having 81mg% in his blood is totally at variance with this principle, as the appendix shows. The harm is increased by the fact that some at least of these lives could be saved in other ways. Thus, for example, the Breathalyser might have saved the lives of the two individuals in the incident at Warmwell Cross, considered above (5.2, p. 39 and 6.11, p. 64), but it would not have saved the other fatalities there, while the roundabout would have saved all of them.

Returning to the matter of road improvements, since the M1 was opened to traffic in 1960, about 550 miles of motorway have been opened. It would not be unreasonable to assume that these roads will have saved at least two hundred lives this year, lives which would have been lost if the motorways had not been opened.

Taken with all the other works on other roads which have been opened in those years, it might not be an overestimate to expect a total reduction of about four hundred lives this year from this source. The saving would have been gradually rising to this figure since 1960. There is little or no sign of this in the published figures, which have been roughly stationary relative to the population and number of motor vehicles since before 1960. It seems probable, then, that there is some influence at work to cancel out the efforts of road engineers. What this is can only be conjectured, but one cannot lightly dismiss the possibility that it could be the effect of the 1960 Act, or possibly also the number of 40 and 50 mile/h speed limits that have been posted recently.

The publication in *The Times* recently of the correspondence in connection with the Hixon level-crossing disaster lends some confirmation to what I have said in many places above, that our rulers tend to think that everything can be blamed on the motorist.

Finally, we are led to another social effect that can hardly be anything but harmful. As we have seen three times in this country, in the U.S.A. with Senator Ribicoff, and in France with M. Bunau (Qu. 10, p. 103) an ambitious politician or official can build up an easy reputation for himself by measures directed at motorists, without troubling whether they will have any real effect, sure in the confidence that any harmful effects can be blamed on the motorist. I am not blaming these people, *they know not what they do*. The blame lies with the public who accept these things. The uncomfortable possibility remains—and Figure 12 (p. 84) and its accompanying discussion show that this possibility is not a remote one—that the only practical effect of Senator Ribicoff's 'crackdown on speeders', as Nader contemptuously called it, was his promotion to the coveted post of United States Senator. If this is so, the one hundred thousand or so people who have lost their licences since 1956 may have some right to feel that the promotion was hardly won.

I will, of course, be accused for disregarding cost in all that has gone before. I fully realize that many of my suggestions for improvements would be very costly, and that we have, as a nation, to consider the priorities between such things as schools, hospitals, roads and so on. It may be fair enough if the nation decides that other things take priority over roads. But the nation must then realize that its decision costs lives, and the present procedure, in which we allow accidents to happen, and then punish the often innocent victims to dull our consciences, is indefensible. We are, in fact, punishing motorists to save money, and not to save accidents. The punishment does not save accidents, it increases them.

September 1968

APPENDIX

STATISTICAL METHODS

THIS Appendix is an extension of Chapter 2. Those who have some elementary algebra may find symbols and diagrams easier to follow.

The symbols used are: x for the variate, a bar over the symbol for its mean, thus x̄, S() for the sum of a number of quantities of the type within the bracket, n for the number, σ for the standard deviation of a population, s for the estimate of it made from a sample, often called the *root mean square.* Then σ will be the *variance* of the population, and s² its estimate from the sample, often called the mean square.

The mean (2.3, p. 9) will be: $\bar{x} = \dfrac{S(x)}{n}$

The difference between any one value of the variate and the mean, (x – x̄), is called a *deviation.* The variance is obtained by first squaring all the deviations and adding them together, which gives a very important quantity called the *sum of squares.* This is then divided by the number of observations to get the variance, so:

$$\sigma^2 = \frac{S(x-\bar{x})^2}{n}$$

Using this method for the estimate of the variance from a sample would tend to give too small a value, so for s² from a sample we divide by the number of *degrees of freedom* in it. This is the number of independent comparisons it contains. This can best be understood by imagining that we have to divide the whole of a number of articles among several people, with complete freedom to give as many as we like to any individual. But this freedom must perforce end at the last person, who must have any remainder. We therefore have one fewer degree of freedom than the number in the sample, that is (n – 1).

This also applies if our recipients are divided into groups, and we have to distribute first among the groups, and then among the individuals composing them. Say we have ten people, divided into two groups of six and four. We will then have one degree of freedom among the groups, and five in the first group and three in the second. But 1 + 5 + 3 = 9 which is the total number among the ten. This always obtains, no matter how the total is subdivided. Then

223

dividing the sum of squares of the sample by the number of degrees of freedom gives us:

$$s^2 = \frac{S(x - \bar{x})^2}{(n-1)}$$

We base much of our work on the *normal distribution* (2.4, p. 11), and because many distributions have properties approximating to it we can do this without serious error. It is shown in the upper curve—the full line—in Figure A1, which is a frequency curve. That is, it shows the frequency, f, of occurrence of any value of the

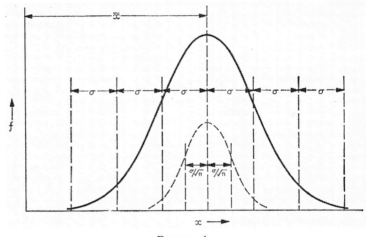

FIGURE A1

variate. Those near the mean will occur most often, with a tailing off—theoretically to infinity—symmetrically in either direction. The dashed vertical lines are separated by amounts equal to the standard deviation. For our practical purposes we can take it that about two-thirds of the observations will be contained within the pair of lines distant σ from the mean, 19/20ths between the 2σ pair, while only 1/400th will be outside the 3σ pair. These express the probabilities of getting values outside these lines, and they constitute the test of significance known as the *normal deviate,* e, which is the deviation divided by the standard deviation. Half these amounts will be outside each of the lines on one side of the mean.

We seldom know σ for the population, and have only s, its estimate from a sample, to use; but in the case of the blood-alcohol test, Sweden has apparently found, as a result of long experience, that it can be taken as 5mg% (11.8, p. 151) so we can use this as an example. If it is so, the upper curve in Figure A1 would represent the result of an infinite number of tests taken from the same person's blood, with σ = 5mg%. We would therefore expect one test in every six to give a value more than 5mg% above or below the mean, one in twenty to give a value more than 10mg% above or below the mean, and one in eight hundred to give one 15mg% above or below. This would mean that if a man had a mean of 65mg%, and so would presumably be legally innocent, once in eight hundred tests he would be found guilty by reason of experimental error. If he had a mean of 95mg% and so was clearly guilty, once in eight hundred times the errors would get him off.

It is, of course, not so clear-cut as that. We would usually have a reading of x mg% sent in by the laboratory, and have no means of finding out the real mean content, apart from taking a large number of samples. The situation might be like that shown in Figure A2, in which the reading from the laboratory is shown with the vertical line. It *could* have come from the tail of either of the two distributions shown, or from any intermediate one.

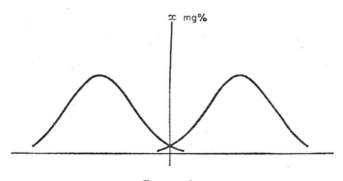

x mg%

FIGURE A2

This is the reason for the practice in Sweden mentioned by Pole (11.8, p. 151) of the laboratories only reporting a test as above the limit if it comes out 15mg%—or three standard deviations—above it. This still leaves the possibility that an innocent man would be convicted once in eight hundred tests.

This principle applies whatever the value of the standard deviation, only the figure given to σ would be changed.

The other tests use the estimate s from the sample, and some also use another principle which has application for us. This is that if we take a large number of random samples from a normally distributed population with variance σ, the means of those samples will themselves be normally distributed with variance σ^2/n. This is shown in Figure A1 in which the main distribution is the upper one—full line—and that of the means of the samples is the dashed smaller one, with its standard deviation of $\sigma/\sqrt{n}$.

This could again apply to the blood-alcohol problem. If the laboratory tested both the samples taken instead of keeping one as a control—which seems to be the proposal—the variations I have discussed above would not be halved, but divided by $\sqrt{2}$, which is 1·41, so they would have a σ of 3·5 instead of 5. If all three samples were used, including that supplied to the accused, the divisor would be $\sqrt{3}$, which would give a new σ of 3. Otherwise all would be as before.

The principle of the tests of significance is that we derive certain functions from the data. These are then looked up in tables which are published in many books, and these give the probability of getting that value of the function from data with that number of degrees of freedom, by random sampling from the same population. Space does not allow of further details, but for those who wish to follow up this very fascinating subject I give four books for further reading. In none of these is more than an elementary knowledge of algebra needed.

Facts from Figures by F. J. Moroney. Penguin 1956. General principles clearly explained. Rather more mathematical.

How to Lie with Statistics by Darrell Huff. Gollancz 1954. A very amusing and lightly written book, no theory, but tells us how we can be deceived.

Statistical Methods for Engineers by J. J. Leeming. Blackie 1963. Deals with practical methods in more detail, and in more mathematical form.

Use and Abuse of Statistics by W. J. Reichmann. Penguin 1964. Mainly general principles easily explained. A little mathematics, but in appendixes.

INDEX